WOKE BITCH

Your Guide to
WELL-BEING

MARISSA HOU

Printed in the USA

First Edition

ISBN: 978-1-955346-05-4

Cover & Layout Design: Heather Dakota
www.heatherdakota.com

Illustrations: Marissa Hou

Wyrd & Wyld Publishing
Spokane, WA

Learn more at
www.marissahou.com

To my family—you are the foundation to my expansion.

To Mom and Dad who embody unconditional love, support, and generosity.

In loving memory of Ah-yu, who dedicated her life to teaching, raising, and loving me.

My nanny, best friend, and so much more.
July 1933 - December 2016

Woke Bitch

YOUR GUIDE TO WELL-BEING

Table of Contents

Hi there,
Thanks for choosing this book!

My cousin Emily and I are around the same age and have lived and partied in NYC since we were 18 years old. Our bathroom counters were full of makeup, false lashes, perfumes, self-tanner, and lotion with shimmer and glitter. The radio blasted New York Hip-hop station Hot 97 as we listened to music, drank vodka and cranberry juice, and got ready for yet another night of dancing and partying. A sign of a good night out was smeared black eyeliner and blisters on our feet from highly uncomfortable yet very "sexy" heels. If it was a wild night—one of those glued-on lashes would come off and show up the next day on a purse or a fabulous piece of clothing we had purchased for the occasion.

During this time, we had serious relationships, pursued higher education degrees, and advanced our careers. I'm not sure when we had time for the spiritual growth and expansion part of life. It happened so gradually. My cousin and I hung out. Doing anything was fun, spontaneous, and filled with laughter.

During a particularly challenging situation, my heart and body cracked open. For me, this was the catalyst. The partying no longer served me and harmed me more than I let on. The pain propelled my growth and forced me to take a closer look at how I was taking care of myself—physically, mentally, emotionally, and spiritually. My suffering created a depth, like the layers of an onion. The more layers I peeled, the more the Universe sent me angels for support. My cousin, who went through her own challenges, met me in these deeper layers. We talked about healing, being present, and living from a place of stillness.

Attending retreats together was something Emily and I enjoyed. In our hotel room at a retreat in Greece, we couldn't help but laugh at our nightstand and TV stand, which we transformed into what we called a Witches' Den. Palo santo sticks and crystals purified the space. Flower essence elixirs and an oracle deck completed our sacred space. Emily and I saw the same nutritionist, so we had a spread of vitamin bottles, magnesium tablets, and digestive enzymes that resembled a Duane Reade pharmacy meets the Witches. With every inch of counter space consumed by our spiritual and wellness goodies, it showed how our priorities had changed in only a few years. We realized that we were the essence of our light, joy, and signature sass far beyond what we owned and how much we partied.

A year after the retreat in Greece, we attended another one in Santa Barbara. This particular year another cousin brought his boyish charm and humor, which added to our fun. Toward the end of the retreat, we had a short break between the sessions, so we jumped into his car and drove to a local coffee shop for coffee and pastries. I mean, who would want hotel food, again! As Emily and I sipped our beverages, I realized that it was time to take our supplements. We each whipped out our supplements and chased them down with our coffees. Very spiritual, I know! My supplements were in my highly fashionable Hello Kitty bag, like a drug dealer with her stash. Again, very spiritual!

Giggling and caffeinated, we joked that we were such "Woke Bitches"—attending retreats, meditating, drinking coffee with pastries, and having a good laugh through it all. We thought we should create a book for others to become a "Woke Bitch"—sharing everything we learned on our journey to awakening to our true selves. It would be fun to share how the challenges of our lives weren't good or bad but helped us see the preciousness of our well-being—a collection of our essential AF lessons learned.

So here I am, writing the book, infusing lessons I've learned from my journey to wokeness.

There's a saying that the teacher arrives when the student is ready. My challenges emptied a space within me that I wanted to fill with more, something more than life had shown me so far. I wanted to know more. I wanted to get to know my true self. There is a feeling that arises that gets you thinking:

Who am I?

What's life all about?

What is enough?

What is beyond?

My core vision is to provide readers with helpful materials in an accessible, funny, and inspiring way. Sure, it's about spirituality and your well-being. If you think this should be taken seriously with a capital "S," then congrats, you met your ego. Maybe your mind told you that spirituality was serious stuff. You must look a certain way (think wearing organic cotton clothing), or feel a particular way (high on meditation) while being "spiritual" or "woke."

Some people may be turned off by choosing to use the word "Bitch" in the title of this book. Others may find that *Woke* is used incorrectly. In the spiritual community, we often talk about "awakening." What the heck does that even mean, you may ask? Life is an illusion. As human beings, we have an infinite well of wisdom and power that is far beyond the appearances and situations we find ourselves in. In this context, *Woke* is a spiritual sense of awakening or waking up to your true self, which is not your ego, mind, or body you were born into. We are all waking up to our true selves and ego all the time.

Life is always presenting opportunities to grow and expand into who we really are beyond appearances and our roles. My path to awakening took me to all types of retreats and workshops. With as many books as I have, I could open a spiritual bookstore. Everything intrigued me and quenched my curiosity. You don't need to follow in my footsteps or study concepts of quantum leaping, frequency, or words you can't pronounce and never heard of to grow and become a "Woke Bitch," too.

You're about to awaken to unique possibilities, spiritual happenings, and your true self. Buckle up! It's going to be the most amazing adventure of your life. This book is broken into four sections: the Mind, Body, Heart, and Spirit, which are integral to your holistic well-being because, hey, you don't want to sell yourself short, bypassing the important stuff that unlocks the power within you!

First, we start playing at the tip of the iceberg examining the mind and body. Then, we'll go deep under the iceberg to look at our hearts and spirits (because that's where it gets juicy and purposeful).

Another way to look at your journey is to work your

way from the tangible, thought forms and physical forms, to what can't be seen with your eyes but is real AF for our fulfillment, such as emotions and spirit. Trust that you're ready for the material in this book, no matter how you choose to use it.

You'll find Easy Exercises (EE), Woke Bitch Challenges (WBC), and Key Takeaways at the end of each chapter. The teacher within wants to make it easy and practical to incorporate the lessons. The EE is quick and simple to explore at any time. The WBC goes deeper into the practices and invites you to try it for a longer period of time. The Key Takeaways are quick chapter recaps.

Again, this is your guide to Well-Being, so practice what speaks to you and have fun!

My greatest hope is that you realize no matter where your life is right now, you're always where you are meant to be, uncovering a deeper you, and awakening to the illusions of what appear to be your external realities. You are already Woke and supported by the love of the Universe. You have permission to be kind to yourself, grow, and feel joy in every moment of every day.

Blessings and Love,
Marissa Hou

Defining God

The word *God* wasn't a word I used two years ago. It never occurred to me to reflect on why I didn't use it. It never had meaning for me. It wasn't until I went through some intense hardships that I cracked open in a way that made me more receptive to something greater than myself. My old ways of striving and accomplishing couldn't help me find peace or make sense of why such intense challenges were happening in my life. Then I paid attention to my spirit and remained open to healing and a different way of living. At first, uttering the word God seemed odd. The word God scared me because others are uncomfortable in the spiritual conversations. Over time, as I woke and remained open to the wonders of this Universe, I came to know God and feel at ease speaking about God and to God daily.

As a reader, you may have a different belief or wording for what is greater than yourself, to which I wholeheartedly say, *good on you*! Use the word that aligns with you. Some words commonly used to express God include: Source, Spirit, the Universe, the Divine, the One, Buddha, Jesus, Allah, the Great Mother, Supreme Being, Brahman, Goddess, The Great Mystery, Great Spirit, and Consciousness. In essence, God can't be defined by a word, and all timeless and infinite wonders can't be captured by our human language. The words I use in this book are pointers for what your soul already knows. The essence and beauty of a rose can't be encompassed when you speak the word *rose* or talk about roses. Your experience of the rose is what stays with you. My experience of God is what stays with me and gives meaning to the word. So, I invite you to remain open and nimble and not be stuck by any word on these pages. To me,

God orchestrates the synchronicities of life, letting me know that I am taken care of by a force that is infinite, powerful, and all-loving.

God is *(use the word that works for you)*

- Universal Great Love
- The Creator
- The Divine
- Sacred
- Omnipotent, Infinite, Omnipresent
- Available always and forever, and accessible NOW
- Only Love
- Universal Strength
- Formless, Timeless
- Your most powerful supporter, available 24/7
- You which is also in me and in all beings
- Always trying to help you grow
- My life, career, wedding, family, and travel planner

God isn't only free of charge, but the most seasoned planner that knows your every hope, heart's desire, and what is best for you.

It took a lot to bring me mentally, emotionally, physically, and spiritually to realize God. Love began filling in the cracks. Every day was filled with wonder, growth, and joy. Life doesn't get any more magical or sacred than that. The falls you take, the pain and wounds that crack you open will point you toward your own knowing of God, saying "Hey, slow down, relax, let *Me* help you."

Transformation from pain and suffering to love and faith is pure magic. Alchemy. God.

As a human beings, we may have cuts, bruises, and wounds from the journey of life. Instead of asking "Why me?" my hope is that you'll soften and let unconditional love in through the wounds and remain open to the Divine forces aiding you All. The. Time.

PART 1:
The Mind

The human mind tends to get stuck in thought, positive and negative. Many people experience a critical voice within the mind, which tells them what they should or shouldn't do or think. My advice: *Don't listen to your inner critic.* Whatever you dream of doing, do it! Don't let your mind stop you.

"The mind can be a beautiful place or a nightmare."
–Michael Singer

We are born and given an incredible tool—the mind—capable of invention, creativity, and making the impossible possible. Everything enhances our lives or makes our lives more convenient and enjoyable has been the result of the human mind. I love traveling, attending retreats, and taking courses online and in-person. These are my favorite products of the human mind.

Are you experiencing a lack of inspiration or creativity? You may be experiencing monkey mind, running on the hamster wheel, or a downward spiral into negative thought. Despite what social media would like us to "think," we all go through this from time to time.

The human mind has a tendency to get stuck in thought, positive and negative. Many people experience a critical voice within the mind, which tells us what we should or shouldn't do or think. When do you experience this critical voice?

A few years ago, I was given the opportunity to co-teach a course in hotel sales to graduate students pursuing their master's degree in Hospitality and Tourism at NYU, my alma mater. The opportunity was exciting, especially since I was a graduate of the same program. I knew that sharing my ten years of practical experience in hospitality would be meaningful to the students. This would be my first time teaching. Creating the presentation and fine-tuning the sessions I taught gave me a lot of joy and energy. The materials and my efforts would make this an engaging class.

The night before class, I couldn't sleep. *Have you experienced this?* The voice in my head wouldn't shut up. What if the students ask a question, and I don't know the answer? What if I look stupid in front of the students? Am I qualified to teach this class? What if I can't find the classroom or my alarm doesn't go off? You are much younger than the other professors at the University. And so, it went on and on for hours. The anxiety built and each sleepless hour brought more thoughts and more anxiety.

When the alarm went off, a deep discomfort in my gut began to roll. I'm sure lack of sleep didn't help. The critical voice was louder than ever. I wanted to send an email to the university to let them know that I wasn't going to make it due to illness. And I seriously considered sending that email. Instead, I got up, got dressed, and went to class with my stomach sitting in my throat.

I have been teaching graduate and undergraduate students for four years. Imagine what would have happened if I had listened to that loud, obnoxious voice in my head. My advice: Do it. Whatever you dream of doing, don't let your mind stop you.

I don't mean to diss the mind because the mind creates amazing stuff. It's the critical and unsupportive voices that create challenges and suffering. These voices don't want your circumstances to change, even if it is an amazing opportunity. These critical voices get really loud when our soul is pushing us to do what we came here to do. The mind wants to keep you safe from the saber-toothed tiger of a new job, writing a book, taking a risk, or sharing your creativity with others.

CHAPTER ONE

Your Thoughts and Being in Your Head

Your mind isn't your enemy. Sometimes it may seem like a wild beast that needs to be tamed, but it isn't. It is a wonder to behold.

Let's be real for a second—take an inventory of everything your mind does for you, such as:

- Helps you breathe
- Produces millions of thoughts
- Creates beauty
- Keeps you safe
- Uplifts the world

The mind is an incredible tool, capable of changing the world, and yet, sometimes it gets us into trouble.

In my own life, I asked too much of my mind. I put it in complete control of my happiness, which means that my mind found a way to manipulate people and situations. *Yikes!* This isn't the responsibility of your mind.

In the coming chapters, we'll look at the tools and techniques to build more awareness, ease the pressure of your mind, and fix your life from the outside-in. Intellectually, you may understand that change and joy happen from the inside out. Don't be overwhelmed by this—celebrate it!

Thank the Universe that your joy and freedom are within and don't depend on outer circumstances.

E² EASY EXERCISE

Good job, Mind!

This Easy Exercise builds appreciation and curiosity around everything the mind invents or creates. By noticing how your car runs, phone charges, and even the craftsmanship of your accessories, you'll celebrate the amazing accomplishments of the mind.

1. Identify something that you use in your daily life.
2. Examine all the functions that this thing serves in your life.
3. Break down the components of this thing. Allow yourself to be curious about how it was made and the thoughts that went into its invention.
4. Express gratitude for this thing in your life and the mind's contribution for bringing this idea to life.

WOKE BITCH CHALLENGE

Hello, you *here*?

Are you here right now? Is your mind consumed with personal narratives of the past or future?

1. Set a timer for one minute or be mindful of the clock for approximately a minute.
2. Watch your thoughts the way you watch a movie.
3. Pay attention to the dialogue and soundtrack of the mind.
4. Make note of the mind's tendency to drift into a past memory or comment on a future event that has yet to happen.
5. Once the minute is up, end your observation.

Bonus: Take notes on how often your mind drifts and where it goes.

 # KEY TAKEAWAYS

- Our minds produce sound bites of thoughts that may or may not be real or true.

- We choose to apply our mind for creativity or destruction (We'll go over how later!)

- Everything we touch in our daily life was created by a mind, so let's celebrate all our minds can do!

CHAPTER TWO

Do I Look Big in this Thought?

Here's a refreshing way to look at thoughts that bring you some clarity. Don't give your thoughts power. Don't believe every thought. You're probably like *whaaat*? How can I not listen to or take my own thoughts seriously? That's not "woke."

Here's a little secret about thoughts. Eckhart Tolle completely blew my mind with "You are not thinking your thoughts." What the heck does that mean? Thoughts are something that arise in your mind. It is the nature of the mind to produce thoughts just as you digest or breathe. This gives you the greenlight to let go of thoughts and give yourself a break. If the mind thinks thoughts, this is not your fault, so allow yourself to chill out. *Please seek professional advice for thoughts of suicide or depression.*

When I understood that I'm not my thoughts, it gave me more peace and clarity because I no longer I had to be a prisoner to my thoughts. During the panic of the changing millennium (1999 to 2000), many people thought that the end of the world was coming and all the computers wouldn't be able to adapt to the changing year. Today, our computers analyze our shopping habits and recommend what we want to keep us buying without thinking.

All types of thoughts happen. It doesn't mean there is truth to every single thought happening in your mind.

For example, you take an exam at school. You finished

the exam, yet your mind is still thinking about the answers. Maybe you talked to a friend after the test, and they chose B for the first question and so did you. Your mind may have a narrative like "this is great, one other person chose the same answer." Maybe you run into another classmate who has historically scored well on other exams and he or she says that the answer is C. Your mind may think, "Oh geez, this person always does well on exams, I got the answer wrong." Then, your mind spirals into "What if I don't score well on this exam? Will I lose my scholarship? If I lose my scholarship, my parents will be so disappointed, and then what will I do?" This is just a simple illustration of how the thoughts that arise through the mind take you on a magic carpet ride that isn't magical at all.

Now look at the facts—the exam is done and in the past. Your thoughts can't change your answers. That's a fact. Here's another golden nugget of wisdom—the thoughts your mind came up with about doing poorly on the exam, affecting your scholarship, disappointing your parents, and leading to failure—feel into the vibration of this storyline. Yikes, feels like shit, huh? This is your imagination gone berserk. These stories created by the mind can't resolve or pacify you, so they spiral into an unholy hell!

At the end of the day, trying to find relief from thoughts by creating more thoughts is a recipe for disaster. It is just thought, not reality! Are you ready to put some distance between your Self and your thoughts?

- Since you are not your thoughts, you can let them go with ease like last season's fashion faux pas.
- Situations are neutral and something that naturally

25

unfolds. Feeling upset over any situation is often a sign that our mind has formed thoughts about the situation, so check yo'self before you wreck yo'self!

The mind experiences 60,000 – 80,000 thoughts per day. Why allow a fraction of them to define who you are? Think of yourself as a vast vessel through which thoughts pass.

"You are the sky, everything else is just the weather."
–Pema Chodron

E^2 EASY EXERCISE

Neutralize the Situation

Allow any current situation come to your mind to be this experiment. How do your thoughts about this situation inform the situation? Does this situation make you feel irritable, attacked, or all-knotted-up? Visualize yourself blasting a big, cool gust of "Neutralizer" on this situation to purify it and remove any thoughts around it. Do you have a new and more spacious take on your situation now?

WOKE BITCH CHALLENGE

Throw that Shit(ty thought) Out

The next time you feel unhappy, moody, irritable, sad, anxious, or fearful, stop, drop, and get rid of that thought.

1. Take five minutes to write down everything your mind is thinking from the factual to the absurd.
2. Crumple up the paper and throw it away.
3. Remember that you have the choice to pay attention to your thoughts or throw them in the trash.

KEY TAKEAWAYS

- Thoughts occur naturally, so don't beat yourself up over them

- Thoughts aren't facts or reality. They are like movies that we can observe.

- The practice of observing your thoughts can create more peace and space.

CHAPTER THREE

Netflix, Chill, and Watch the Thoughts

It is one thing to be an observer of your thoughts. Can you go beyond your thoughts and watch them without needing or wanting to change them?

Consider this:

- The heart beats through you. You don't talk to your heart and say "hey, beat for me!" It's a function that happens naturally because we have amazing bodies.
- The digestive system digests on its own.
- The mind produces thoughts, which arise naturally. This is how the mind operates.

You are not fully in control of your mind or body. What a relief! Imagine if you got busy and forgot to breathe—*Yikes!*

We can marvel at the human body and how it naturally functions (digesting, breathing, beating, eliminating waste) and apply these same wonders to the human mind.

E^2 **EASY EXERCISE**

For One Second

Stop for one second as you're reading this. Notice one thought.

- If you have been able to watch your thoughts—even just a single thought—Congratulations! You are an observer. Why is this a special power?

- Through your ability to watch your thoughts, you are no longer the thought. You are the watcher of those thoughts. If you were your thoughts, you would not be able to observe them. *Poof! Mind blown!*

WOKE BITCH CHALLENGE

Hakuna Mattata

Take a no worries, problem free philosophy. Most of us loved this song in *The Lion King*, and now we can love it even more because it's equally effective as it is catchy. The situation we find ourselves in isn't the problem. It's our thoughts about the situation that cause the problem.

Let's explore how situations are neutral, and how our thoughts turn the situation into a problem.

1. Consider a "problem" you are currently experiencing.
2. Allow your mind to go all out about the aspects of this situation and the problems that have arisen due to the situation.
3. Switch gears and say *"Hakuna Mattata"* out loud or yell it if you wish.
4. Revisit the problem on your mind and imagine extracting the mind's commentary, your thoughts. How does the problem feel now? Is the situation neutral without your thoughts?
5. Now, allow yourself to reflect on the perceived problem as a situation.
6. For extra credit, purge the word "problem" from your vocabulary and replace it with "situation" instead.

KEY TAKEAWAYS

- The practice of observing your thoughts is about watching them with curiosity and non-judgment.

- Observing and noticing your thoughts is a step toward inner freedom and liberation from suffering.

- Situations are not problems. They are thoughts. And the thought isn't you, so you're free.

CHAPTER FOUR

Power of Thoughts

I'm sure you have heard that thoughts are powerful. That's great and all, but what's the big deal? They aren't as powerful as Wonder Woman, right?

A few years ago, I was at a Flower Essences workshop and learned about a study by Dr. Emoto, a scientist who studies water. His studies focused on how the molecular structure of water changed based on the words the water was exposed to. Let's say we spoke to a glass of water (yes, talk to the water) every day for a week saying, "You are beautiful. I love you." Then, we told a different glass of water, "You disgust me. I hate you." Dr. Emoto's findings are probably no surprise. Which glass of water do you think formed beautiful crystal structures, and which one formed disconnected and twisted structures?

The water molecules exposed to love, kindness, and compassion formed beautiful crystal structures. This study encourages us to pay more attention to our thoughts and our rhetoric toward ourselves. Human beings are comprised of seventy-percent water. Each thought that comes to our mind and the words we say to ourselves through thoughts can alter our physical body. Wild, right?

Mantras are popular and powerful. As we repeat the mantra, it creates a new reality. You may think, well, I have spent 20 years thinking unkind thoughts and judging my appearance in the mirror, I must be messed up beyond repair. You're not beyond repair! You can change your rhetoric now and allow yourself to grow and improve. Dr. Emoto's studies also showed that prayer can transform unpleasant looking water's molecular structure into a beautiful one.

E² EASY EXERCISE

Mind yo language

A simple swap of *I want* instead of *I don't want* allows you to feel into the power of words and how your body responds to them just like water molecules do. Yes! The ones in your body.

1. Practice a few statements right now and notice how each one feels. Instead of focusing on what you don't want, express what you do want and observe how different this feels.
2. Say, *I don't want to be* ____. (Choose a word that reflects a situation you want to improve). How does this statement make you feel? Which word is the emphasis on this statement?
3. Now say, *I want* _____. How does this statement resonate with you? Do you feel more empowered?
4. Explore the two versions of the statements.
5. For extra credit, repeat the positive statement for a week, whenever you think of it, and see how you feel.

WOKE BITCH CHALLENGE

Drop a loving DM

If prayer and beautiful intentions have the power to help others and you, create your own prayer practice.

Step 1: Take a few conscious breaths accepting where you are in this moment.
Step 2: Think of the person / Being / group you would like to offer a prayer. This can be you, too.
Step 3: Visualize this Being. Ask yourself: *What message will bring the most kindness and comfort to this Being right now?*
Step 4: Say your intention for kindness, compassion, and love as a prayer for this Being. TIP: Put one or both hands on your heart. This small act helps amplify the sincerity of your prayer.
Step 5: Thank yourself for taking the time to send good thoughts out into the world. The world always needs your kindness, compassion, and empathy.

Apply this practice to anything and anyone in the world—from your teachers to strangers, the ground beneath your feet to the birds flying overhead. No limits here, baby! When you pray for someone you're being challenged by, this practice is especially powerful. Get witchy with it!

KEY TAKEAWAYS

- Our thoughts have the power to influence our physical bodies.

- The practice of speaking and thinking kind words result in feelings of peace and ease.

- Mantras are a simple, customizable tool for amplifying the goodness of life.

CHAPTER FIVE

Mind Games

The mind has the tendency to create stories and seek to feel good all the time. Your thoughts lead you to feel elated one minute and rock bottom the next. We've already noticed our thoughts. Now, let's go beyond and into the Mind Games.

Ever notice that your mind is like a music playlist on repeat? There's constant background noise and activity. This background noise is the nature of the mind. This is called *monkey mind*. Your thoughts are the songs that make up your playlist. Unlike the actual playlist, it's not easy for the mind to skip a song or thought you're not digging. Some songs make you feel elated, while others remind you of dark times. The next thing you know, you're sucked into a period of wallowing at a pity party for yourself. Raise your hand if you've attended that party.

The thoughts in your head are exactly like the songs. They get you high one moment and drag you down the next. Then you notice these downer thoughts and try to generate another set of thoughts to uplift you. What a roller coaster ride!

Example: You're experiencing heartache

Oh, I'm so sad s/he/they rejected me.

It's okay, s/he's/they're a jerk anyway, I deserve better.

But I miss her/him/them. Now I'm sad again.

Let me see what's on Instagram.

On IG: Oh, cute shirt—I wonder where I can get this! (Scroll, scroll…come across another image)

Oh damn, I'm sad again. I went to this place with her/him/them. Now, I feel bad all over!

Get it? This is the game we play in our minds—that never-ending thought playlist. To constantly feel "up" isn't sustainable and is exhausting AF. So is being sucked into the emo. Love songs aren't a solution either.

So, how do we end this crazy game/monkey mind?

We *wake up* to the game. We realize within ourselves that this is a game and not who we are. This mind game isn't real, so don't take it seriously or treat it as reality.

Wake up to the game through noticing your thought playlist, and don't get involved with the lyrics. Come back to your surroundings, right now.

Note: If you are experiencing symptoms of depression, please seek professional mental health advice.

E² EASY EXERCISE

Snap out of the Game

1. Pause whatever you're "doing" now.

2. Sit up, look around, and tune into your environment. What do you hear? What do you see? Taste? Touch? Smell?

3. As you tune into your surroundings through your senses, challenge yourself to notice something new and beautiful.

4. Take a minute to revel in the beauty and uniqueness of this sight, sound, touch, taste, or smell.

5. Pay it a compliment out loud or within.

6. Notice how you feel.

7. Congrats! You have just completed an exercise to snap out of the mind game and tune into the present moment.

WOKE BITCH CHALLENGE

Beautify your words, beautify your thoughts

You're invited to pay attention to your thoughts and your stories. The next time you look in the mirror, practice saying out loud or in your head, "You're beautiful. I love you." If this is too much for you—come up with your own version of a kind and compassionate line to offer yourself. Mantras are a great way to kick mind games to the side and start feeling good from the inside out. Here are some of my favorite mantras and sayings to feel nourished.

- All is well.
- Thank you for this moment.
- I am loved.
- I am enough.
- I am light from the fire of creation.

KEY TAKEAWAYS

- The mind's tendency is to gravitate toward feeling good no matter the cost.

- The monkey mind involves incessant thinking, evoking moods, which happens to all of us!

- Waking up to the game that our mind plays means we are no longer in the game—yay!

CHAPTER SIX

Equanimity—Resting Bitch Face for the Mind

Equanimity. Wow, a big fancy word that sounds super holier than thou. Spiritual books use the word equanimity all the time. At some point, every spiritual talk includes the word, too. What the heck is up with that?

Equanimity is cultivating a sense of peace within you, especially if you're under stress. Oh yeah, we can all get behind that, am I right?

Exhibit A: My first direct experience with equanimity was when I went on a 10-day silent Vipassana meditation retreat in central Taiwan. It was probably one of the most challenging experiences of my life in many ways. For 10-days in a camp-like setting, we observed noble silence (no talking). In addition, we learned the unique practice of *Vipassana*, which is a meditation technique that the Buddha practiced more than 2,500 years ago. In addition to 10 days of silence, we also observed a monastic lifestyle and strict schedule. Our day started at 4:30 AM with meditation, which lasted about 10 hours. There was no technology allowed. If you're breaking out in a cold sweat over the lack of technology, hold onto your hats. There's more.

The primary teaching of Vipassana is cultivating equanimity. When we sat down each day to meditate and observe our bodies, all types of sensations came up. My legs went numb, ants crawled on me, my back hurt, and my mind thought of everything unpleasant. It was an endless endeavor to sit in silence without fidgeting. Living in silence for 10 days gave my mind plenty of time to play with crazy thoughts to cause imbalances. During my practice, each time I felt discomfort, I consciously practiced being okay in the discomfort. We were cultivating a peaceful space within so there would be no difference in my state of peace whether I felt intense back pain or a pleasant tingling sensation.

During the human lifetime, we encounter all types of situation and sensations. Our minds label them as "good" or "bad," but they still exist. Imagine all of the things you experience in a day, a friend doesn't call you back like they said they would, your flight gets canceled, you run into your favorite celebrity and get a selfie with him or her, or your company gives you an award recognizing your achievements. These are a few examples of things that happen that we could label as *bad* to *good, unpleasant* to *pleasant*. Each experience leaves you feeling and thinking a certain way. If you felt awful about the flight cancellation, you may wish that it never happen again. You may wish that each time you return to the restaurant where you met the celebrity, that a meeting of some sort would happen again and give you that high.

Equanimity gives us the inner spaciousness to be peaceful no matter what happens. At the end of the day, with inner balance, no situation disturbs your inner peace. Simply put—you aren't as bothered by things in general and life experiences unfold as they do, but your happiness is not dependent on the label. Your peace is within and life is on an even keel. As spiritual teacher and psychologist Tara Brach puts it, "Equanimity is a heart ready for anything."

E^2 EASY EXERCISE

All the feels

There is a Zen current that runs through you in all of life's circumstances. When you receive news or information that ruffles your feathers, break out this quick exercise.

1. Tune into your body. Notice where in your body that the information is felt most strongly.
2. Notice the tendency to judge or label the sensation in your body.
3. Take one conscious breath in and out while allowing yourself to feel the sensation as it is.
4. Well done! Your inner balance is growing.

Bonus Points: Take this exercise further. Sense other areas of your body with a conscious, spacious, and balanced state of mind.

WOKE BITCH CHALLENGE

RBF (Resting Bitch Face) for the heart

You know what I mean by this. Call it poker face, call it RBF (more fun I believe)—the point is that with practice, you'll allow your heart to remain in a state of openness and peace that is unshakeable to what happens externally.

Try this experiment:

1. The next time you find yourself getting flustered over anything, practice observing your reaction to it. Take a deep breath and consciously relax, imagining a sense of equanimity where your inner peace can't be disturbed. You can call this your happy place.

2. The same exercise can be done for something that brings you bliss or elation. Can you sense the undercurrent of peace that lies beneath your OMG, this is totally awesome?

3. Appreciate and be present with the experience, but also observe the peace that already exists within, the peace that can't be disturbed or amplified based on external experiences.

KEY TAKEAWAYS

- Equanimity is a state of inner peace available to all of us, no matter what's going on outside.

- The mind's tendency to label things or situations as "good" or "bad" often rocks our equanimity.

- The practice of consciously relaxing with a current situation strengthens equanimity.

CHAPTER SEVEN

Meditation

Everyone can meditate. Period. End of sentence. And for you "rule breakers," there are no rules when it comes to meditation.

Here are some excuses why you may not want to meditate regularly:

- It's about eliminating thoughts from occurring or to "stop thinking," which is impossible.
- Once you sit down to meditate, distracting thoughts occur, and you stop the practice.
- You are afraid of failing or messing up.
- You may not know what to do or how to do it.
- You don't have enough time.

Okay, hold your horses there. The essence of meditation isn't about stopping your thoughts. If anyone can do that, I'd like to meet them. Remember, we said that thoughts arise just as the body breathes on its own. Thoughts are a natural function of the mind. How you relate to your thoughts is where meditation helps. Okay, now we're getting somewhere.

Top tips for meditating:

- When you sit down to meditate, visualize yourself as the observer that is watching clouds pass. The clouds are your thoughts, and you are the sky. Continue to be the observer in the background watching what unfolds in front of you. Be aware of how the mind tries to identify with your thoughts.
- When your mind drifts off into thought, notice it, and come back to your breath. Be mindful without criticizing yourself. Thoughts of criticism are more thoughts. Let them go.
- During meditation, notice the voice in your head commenting on everything. The voice may raise doubt about whether you turned off the stove, or judgment about your practice, or thinking about what you are going to do after meditation. Be glad that you noticed this voice because it isn't you.
- Pay attention to your senses to take the focus away from your thoughts. What do you hear? What is the loudest sound you hear? What is the faintest sound? How about your sense of smell? Feel the breath moving in and out of your body. Is there a taste in your mouth? Does something catch your eye?
- When you notice your senses, you'll see that the thoughts aren't as loud. It's very difficult to be lost in thought while at the same time tuning into your senses and breath.

Meditation, like any practice, gets stronger with practice. Start with a few minutes a day. Your breath is always available as a tool to cultivate space within your mind.

Benefits of a meditation practice:

- Reduces stress and anxiety
- Cultivates self-love and compassion
- Encourages responses to situations and people as opposed to reacting
- Strengthens your intuition and gut instinct
- Regulates your body's breath, nervous system, and digestive system
- Develops a connection to God or the Divine within
- Dissolves a sense of alienation or feeling alone

OCB (One Conscious Breath)

By far, my fave Easy Exercise because anyone can do it anywhere and the reward is fulfilling AF.

1. Consciously and mindfully take one breath, right now.
2. Feel the length of the inhale and the length of the exhale.
3. Notice the quality of your breathing when you are fully present in consciously inhaling and exhaling.
4. Congrats, my friends, you are meditating!

Bonus: Take OCB (one conscious breath) before you leave the house and upon your arrival home. It gives a sense of gratitude.

WOKE BITCH CHALLENGE

Eleven minutes for 30 days

Ready to develop a meditation practice? Set a timer for eleven minutes and meditate, everyday for 30 days to incorporate this habit. If you find the alarm on your phone jarring, download an app, such as Insight Timer, which has nicer sounds like gongs and chimes to use for this practice.

1. Commit to sitting upright and comfortably as your timer begins.
2. During your meditation, be the watcher of your thoughts.
3. Consider your breath as an ally, always ready and willing to support you in coming back to the present moment.
4. Reflect on how you feel after 30 days of practice and follow your soul for next steps.

KEY TAKEAWAYS

- Everyone can meditate.

- Meditation isn't about stopping your thoughts during a sitting; meditation is sitting with your thoughts.

- A regular meditation practice strengthens your physical well-being to alleviate feelings of stress and overwhelm.

CHAPTER EIGHT

Is Your Happiness an Outside Problem or Inside Job?

Ever heard of the saying "happiness is an inside job?" I heard this and thought I had to "do" something to make myself happy and not look to others or things to make me happy. There is some truth to this, but it's misleading. I used to look at this saying with an emphasis on external possessions. For example, I believed that owning a particular material item, such as a pair of shoes, would bring me the happiness I was seeking. I thought buying the shoes with *my money* was the "inner" work. Happiness was an inside job because I took care of the bill on my own. Finally, I realized that it doesn't matter who bought what because I was still attributing my happiness to something outside of myself— the material thing, *you know?* No relationship you have or item you own will bring you happiness, even though you may think so in the moment.

Recently, I took an online course with Michael Singer, author of *The Untethered Soul* and *The Surrender Experiment*. One of my biggest takeaways was examining my own beliefs on what makes me happy? C'mon, I know you have that list stashed away, too. Common ticket items to happiness include a big house, fancy car, attractive partner, children, a dream job. Having our dream means we'll complain less as the thing brings us ultimate fulfillment and happiness, right? Our mind is fixated on the thing instead of being happy with what is. What if you got the dream job and it was more demanding of your time and energy, and you lost your life's balance? Would you still want the dream job?

Here's the light of truth: We don't want these things and situations—we want the happiness and joy that we believe these things, relationships, and jobs will bring us. We want to feel okay inside. *Are you with me so far?*

As human beings, we want the state of happiness within, but look to the outside world instead of within us. Nothing outside of you is going to fix the problem.

So back to the saying that "happiness is an inside job." Here's the secret to happiness. Are you ready? There is nothing you need to do to get the happiness you want except let go of your limiting beliefs. When we begin to rewire and understand that our happiness and joy is a natural state of being, no one and nothing will move us from that state. *Not convinced?*

It's okay. It's natural. Most of us have been raised with certain values and conditions that motivate us to want certain things and be in certain types of relationships. The notion of happiness as an internal state is radical AF. You may be reading this and in the middle of your PhD program and think—*damn, I worked all these years on an external thing thinking it was going to make me happy?* Please don't throw in the towel. You are exactly where you are meant to be, doing exactly what you were meant to do. However, don't expect the PhD to bring you happiness.

You have a level of awareness that is profound and powerful. That alone is profound and powerful. The next time you fixate on wanting something, create some distance, and ask yourself, "What am I believing about this? Do I believe that losing 15 lbs. will bring me happiness? That going on an annual vacation to the Caribbean will make me happy? That the wedding of my dreams will give me eternal happiness?" Become curious about your beliefs and behaviors and happiness will follow like magic. And when you notice that your mind believes that these things will make you happy, be kind and compassionate and recognize it's okay that the mind believes this. When I fixate on making a perfect presentation, I get tense and place a lot of pressure on myself and the future event unfolding in a certain way. On the other hand, if I ask myself, "What if...?" it usually brings me back to an inner state of being with less pressure on the event or situation having to unfold in a certain way. The result is more happiness and joy while building self-compassion. Try it. You'll like it.

Research shows, "Americans are the unhappiest they've been in 50 years. Only 14 percent of adults in the U.S. say they're happy."

E^2 EASY EXERCISE

Untangling your worries

1. List something you're worried about right now (and yes, just one please).

2. Examine it. Ask yourself if your mind emphasized this thing you're worried about as being critical to your happiness or success.

3. Thank yourself for doing this Easy Exercise and being curious about your inner happiness. Your curiosity lightens the pressure the mind carries.

WOKE BITCH CHALLENGE

Challenging your "Happiness"

This is an ongoing practice from the Easy Exercise.

1. Practice the steps in the Easy Exercise above.

2. Take it a step further and identify the thing you're fixated on that you believe leads to happiness.

3. Challenge that thing to a duel by asking, "If (the thing that I'm fixated on) was perfect and real, and I was unhappy, would I still want it?"

4. This challenge can be anything—big or small! If I always wanted perfect hair and finally had perfect hair, but was unhappy about spending three hours

on my hair every day, would I still want perfect hair? Other examples to explore are your dream job, relationships, titles, grades, weight, any dream, big or small, will do.

5. Explore these scenarios for as long as you wish and notice how reframing your beliefs makes you feel.

KEY TAKEAWAYS

- True happiness is a state that is experienced within your sense of Self and doesn't rely on your belongings, titles, relationships, or accomplishments.

- Lasting and true happiness is a state that happens on the inside separate from external situations.

- Reframing your mind and beliefs about what will make you happy is one step toward taking your power back.

CHAPTER NINE

It's Your Choice, Baby!

Every day you have the chance to make new and different choices for yourself from the possibilities and opportunities presented. You have to allow yourself to see them.

While many events in your life may feel completely out of your control, I invite you to explore all the choices. These choices lead you to even more possibilities and opportunities. You may think that it's too late for you, that you're too old or spent a chunk of time on something that doesn't spark joy or happiness. Or that you don't have it in you to change because of your circumstances or history. I'm going to call "Bullshit."

You can begin again, even right now in this very moment. The false messages and stories you've been living with for most of your life are just that…stories. I know. It's hard to rewire these stories because your mind has accepted these stories as truth or fact.

All of us have stories. One of my false beliefs (that I've been unloading) is the belief that I am not fit to live in Taiwan. My crazy thought narrative goes like this:

- It's too hot and humid here.
- My body won't acclimate.

- I have received an American education my whole life, so I belong in America.
- I won't be able to form deep friendships in Taiwan.
- My job opportunities are elsewhere because people won't want to hear an American-born Taiwanese teach a class or lead a workshop.
- I've been successful in NYC for the past 16 years, so that is where my success stays.
- Overall, I am of no value or worth in Taiwan.

These crazy stories came on strong when I found myself in Taiwan due to a global pandemic. They repeated loudly and constantly, increasing my fear and anxiety. I was a victim to the circumstances and was unable to motivate myself to do anything because I believed I was useless and worthless in Taiwan. It was crushing and heavy to wake up each day in this pool of unworthiness that I created. Yes, I created! Then I took it day-by-day, moment-by-moment. One-by-one, I unraveled the narratives. Instead of dwelling on the pandemic and travel restrictions, which I had no control over, I focused on taking everything bite-sized through digesting only what was immediately in front of me. I realized that days devoid of joy were not fun and quite awful. No one wants shitty days. I made little choices to infuse more joy into each day. I took a weekly oil painting class and a restorative stretch class. These classes helped motivate me and quieted the stories that were lodged in my mind. By focusing and making choices around my joy and happiness instead of my worry and fears, I adopted an attitude that each day was an opportunity for me to exercise choices for my highest and best self. These choices are always available whether it's a global pandemic, or you think opportunities and possibilities have passed you by. You always have a choice, and usually several of them.

Fast forward a few months, I was still living in Taiwan and the Universe blessed me. I taught three workshops to the public—one sponsored by the Taiwanese Government on the hotel industry and two sponsored by an arts and culture foundation and a local Taiwanese university on the topic of International Etiquette. After 15 years of not driving, I drove again, made new Taiwanese friends, lived alone in an apartment, made active steps to spend quality time with my parents, and adopted two rescue puppies. It felt as if the Universe gave me kudos each time I showed up. Each baby step led me down a blessing-paved path.

Your life can change by one choice you make. When you shift your focus from your false beliefs, the Universe makes what's needed available and allows you to knock down the limited narratives to create a different reality. I invite you to examine what you're focusing on and seize the opportunities that start presenting themselves. How do you know that these opportunities will show up? Have faith that the Universe will show you where you need to grow.

When you challenge your false beliefs, these stories don't stand a chance to stop you from living your best life right now.

One of my favorite inspiring moments of dismantling limiting patterns and starting anew include my parents. Not long ago, my 70-year-old father asked me to teach him how to meditate. Now, he practices mindfulness each day. My mother exercised for the first time in her sixties. She's much more agile than when she started, proof that what you practice gets stronger. You're never too old *(or young!)* to begin again.

E² EASY EXERCISE

Upgrade Yo Speech

False stories and limiting beliefs eat away at the joy and growth of each moment. I invite you to turn a limiting belief into an opportunity without judgment. Let this be a practice of being kind to yourself, not to "succeed." One way to shift an old story into kindness is being mindful with words.

Instead of "I have to," replace with the phrase, "I choose to" and notice how you feel. This Easy Exercise is a simple shift in speech that results in fempowerment.

1. List 3-5 things that you would describe as things you have to do.
2. Now out loud, replace "I have to" with "I choose to" for what you listed and observe the shift from feeling passive and obligated to empowered.

WOKE BITCH CHALLENGE

Breakthrough False Beliefs ASAP

Shining the spotlight on your false beliefs is uncomfortable and often quite sticky. Your stories don't want to be unstuck. Avoid putting expectations on yourself or getting down on yourself if you think you aren't "good enough" at breaking through these patterns. This is just the mind again!

Below is a list of questions to explore. Get curious and build awareness around your stories and narratives and move beyond them. Inquiries are a fierce way to burst the false-belief bubbles that guide you back to being the Woke Bitch that you are. I invite you to look at the list of questions below or come up with your own. Explore the question(s) that speak to you. Set aside ten minutes to free write your answers. At the end of ten minutes, take a conscious breath. Then, revel in your answers.

- What is a choice you can make right now to improve the situation?
- What narrative is playing on your mind? How does it make you feel?
- Does the narrative in your head relate to the past or future? If so, bring your attention back to the present moment.
- Is what you're worrying about in this moment something that is being experienced by others?
- How can you use this experience to grow?
- What are you dwelling on that doesn't make you feel well?

Shift your attention to the opportunities available to shake up this false belief and challenge it.

KEY TAKEAWAYS

- Focus your actions and intentions on what you can do (no matter how little) to activate positive change.

- Choices are available to you in every moment of every day.

- Opportunities and possibilities are available. When you choose to welcome them into your life, this choice amplifies your connection to the Universe.

What to do when your critical voice is super loud?

- Recognize this voice isn't you. Phew!
- Ask yourself: Is the voice's story one of doubt, fear, or insecurity? If yes, then it's not you.
- When you are about to grow and expand, know that the voice gets especially loud. What a relief.
- Thank the voice. Take a conscious breath and drop your shoulders. The critical voice is only a story.

CHAPTER TEN

Loneliness

Facing and overcoming the fear of loneliness may be one of the biggest life lessons you'll ever have to overcome. There was a time not too long ago when the hardest thing for me was to be at home by myself without plans. Quiet time at home created feelings of loneliness. Does this sound like you? Are your days jam-packed with workouts, happy hours, networking events, dates with a partner or friends, family time, and you want to write a book, paint a masterpiece, or some other creative endeavor? It is exhausting. Why do we do this to ourselves?

Looking at the calendar and the to-do list full of events somehow gave me a false sense of security. The tiredness in my body was a distraction from facing the loneliness in my mind. The distraction of all the plans and the fatigue in my body was better than being home alone.

Speaking of distractions, a series of longer-term relationships distracted me from examining my "stuff." The loneliness of the mind I experienced moved into my relationships, too. Although the past partners and I parted, I rarely spent time by myself and later observed that I had a deep fear of being alone. When you're alone, you have to face thoughts of being unlovable, incomplete, or unworthy. Relationships were an easy way to get distracted from the shadows I didn't want to face. Of course, being in a relationship didn't silence those thoughts either. The common denominator was me and the underlying issues were my own thoughts and fears generated by narrative after narrative. It's no wonder that partners never make us completely at ease or whole even though we experience moments of joy and happiness. Ease and wholeness come from within and can't be fulfilled by any other person.

After realizing that I had a fear of being alone, I broke up with a partner of almost three years. I knew in my heart that I wasn't in love but hiding from loneliness. What I wasn't prepared for was the pain after the breakup. All my wounds were magnified, and it hurt just to be awake because facing insecure thoughts, fears, and doubts is painful. There is no way around the pain. You have to face it.

I was woke enough to know better than to turn to alcohol, food, drugs, or another romantic partner. I wasn't sure how to deal with heartache in a "spiritual" way. I wrote into a live Q&A. The Universe came through and my question was selected to be the one answered live. I was nervous and excited. To this day, I listen to this precious recording of my question being answered. Here were my key takeaways:

- No one can complete you.
- When you lean on another person, and the other person needs space, you collapse. You must learn to stand on your own.
- When you feel pain after a heartache, your thoughts may sound like this: *"I'm x number of age, what if I'm alone forever? What if I don't find someone?"* Thoughts like these are fear talking. You don't have to believe in your thoughts, they are just thoughts!
- If you don't face your fears of being alone, you may

find yourself in the same type of relationship like the one that just ended.

- The relationship you are seeking isn't with another, but with your true self. The true self that is beyond ego, thoughts, personality, and circumstances.

The emotion behind heartache is loss. There was something in your life and now it's not—it's natural to feel loss and sadness. However, I was reminded to not wallow or swim in the swamp of narratives of not finding someone or being incomplete alone. These were stories and not who I am.

I made progress by leaps and bounds facing my fears of being alone. This past year, I spent most of my time alone and came to enjoy it. To be in stillness, listen to my inner voice, have no plans and allow life to unfold in front of me, being by myself, and experiencing joy in solitude helped me dissolve the fear of loneliness. Every day I practice seeing the wholeness within me. Now, anyone who comes into my life as a partner would be the cherry on top of the sundae. I am the sundae!

The Universe gives us opportunities to learn lessons and heal pain. Although I have healed a lot of fears surrounding being alone, a Woke Bitch's job is never done. There are times when the narrative of being alone the rest of my life rears its ugly head and grabs me by the wrist, and forces me to go down that fear-based rabbit hole again. If you find yourself in those times, return to the present moment. Feel what you're feeling, but don't wallow in it. Don't get stuck in the muck of your thoughts.

If you have a fear of being alone or feel lonely, you aren't alone (pun intended).

E² EASY EXERCISE

Solo Self-Love

Feel complete and whole through solo self-love.

1. Take a moment to reflect on what activities or gestures come to mind when you think of self-love.

   - Check out a new restaurant, exhibit, attraction, or store where you've wanted to go.
   - Take a device-free walk with no destination, and allow your heart to lead the way.
   - Enjoy your reading material leisurely and without distractions.
   - Sit in the sun and enjoy a yummy beverage.
   - Attend a favorite class of any sort (movement, art, writing, new skill).

2. Carve time in your calendar to begin your chosen activity within the next week. Let the idea of this upcoming activity delight you.
3. Be open to modifying the activity until it sparks joy.
4. Be open to modifying the activity as guided. For example, taking an art class might be what came to mind for you. If the art class isn't something you can do in a week or so, allow yourself to pick up a new sketchbook and draw this week.

WOKE BITCH CHALLENGE

Tacklin' Loneliness?

Sharpen observation skills, create space from your own loneliness, and enhance curiosity over self-criticism. You've got this!

1. Suddenly, a familiar ache begins. Something is "not okay" with you being alone in this moment.
2. Question your loneliness- for example, you are in your apartment on a Friday night and suddenly overcome by this feeling of loneliness that results in maybe nervousness or a feeling in the stomach or chest. If this example doesn't apply to you, think of a situation that has made you feel lonely. You do you.
3. Question your loneliness. Before every feeling or sensation, there is a thought. What is the story you're telling yourself? Be watchful and mindful of these stories and thoughts. Is a narrative running that you shouldn't be home alone on a Friday? Are you thinking that you'll never find someone? Thoughts lead to feelings, but you're not your thoughts or your feelings.
4. Recognize that the "loneliness" is fueled by false thoughts you have in this moment and they will go away. When you are aware of the stories you tell yourself, you gain space. In that space, you'll find your freedom.

5. Be gentle, kind, and curious about your fears surrounding loneliness. Accept that there may be a pattern or conditioning you are working through. Give yourself credit for your efforts.

KEY TAKEAWAYS

- Loneliness is a state of mind experienced by all of us.

- The cure for loneliness doesn't involve being in relationship with another being.

- Spending time alone and recognizing the beautiful qualities within you can strengthen your confidence and defeat loneliness. I mean, come on, you're awesome!

SHOW YOUR FEAR SOME LOVE.

PART 2:
The Body

The body is a beautiful vessel that holds our vitality and is constantly sending you signals and feeding you information, so you can live your best life. Treat your body with respect, love, and compassion, and watch your well-being expand into all areas of your life.

CHAPTER ELEVEN

The Mind and Body are Homies

You've heard of the mind-body connection, right? Well it's a real thing! The mind and body are homies with a tight bond before science was onto them. When we build awareness with our thoughts as the observer, we also begin to observe sensations in the body as well. When an unhappy thought arises, we may feel a pit in our stomach or nausea may develop. If the thought is one of grief, a sinking feeling may arise, or we may lose our appetite. Fearful thoughts trigger a fight, flight, or freeze response manifesting in a quickened heart rate, sweating, and tension. I know this all sounds so shitty, but our thoughts manifest in wondrous sensations, too. Loving and kind thoughts generate ease in our body. After a meditation practice or reading, a spiritual connection resonates and causes joyful vibrations in our bodies.

Your thoughts show up in your body. It's all connected. There is an exchange of information with each element (mind, body, heart, and soul) vibing off each other like an awesome jazz band. When you hear the music and watch them play, you can tell that they are in sync with one another—all perfectly timed.

The mind and body are tightly connected. Therefore, it's worth exploring the quality and nature of your thoughts and how they relate to certain areas of your body. Some teachers say that each discomfort and shitty sensation in the body has an emotional root. For example, if you experience indigestion or cramps in the stomach, this may be a cue to ask if there are any experiences or feelings, you're having a tough time digesting. Upon reflection, you may want to offer your body some extra TLC and say something soothing to ease your stomach area and the tension you're experiencing. Because everything is connected, healing our thoughts and thought patterns is a great opportunity to bring our mind and body into better alignment.

I can get nerdy about this stuff, but it is truly fascinating how the mind shows up in our emotional, physical, and spiritual bodies. It's also uplifting to discover that we have infinite ways to heal ourselves. Whether we start with our thoughts or a physical symptom, we can allow these to guide us to our well-being.

E^2 EASY EXERCISE

Flexing Your Mind-Body Connection Muscle

To experiment and observe the body's response to thoughts...

1. Think of your favorite person, pet, or thing.
2. Notice how you feel within your body. Is there a feeling of joy or being uplifted?
3. Think of a piece of news or information that makes you sad.
4. Notice how this thought makes you feel in your body.
5. Reflect on how different thoughts manifest in your body. Feel free to experiment going back and forth between thoughts and bodily sensations.

WOKE BITCH CHALLENGE

Hacking Your Mind-Body Connection

Notice your body's response to thoughts and insert uplifting thoughts to shift gears from hell-no to hell-yeah!

1. Complete Steps 1-5 in the Easy Exercise.
2. For the thoughts that make you sad, pay close attention to which part of the body feels the thought most. (Example: a tightness in the stomach).
3. Take a few slow breaths. Ask yourself what comforting words or thoughts would help to pivot away from the negative sensations.
4. Practice saying the words you have come up three times and notice how you feel. Here are some examples:

All is well.

I'm okay in this moment.

I have everything I need to get through this.

I am safe and healthy.

I can heal myself.

KEY TAKEAWAYS

- Your thoughts and emotions have a direct link with your physical body.

- Many ailments have mental and emotional causes that can be healed through recognizing and improving our thought patterns.

CHAPTER TWELVE

Let's Get Heavily Meditated!

Here's the thing about a meditation practice—you're probably already doing it, and don't even know it, because it doesn't look like the Google results for "meditation."

Meditation strengthens inner peace, joy, and being in the present moment. We've already talked about meditation being great for the mind, but it does wonders for the body, too. *Remember, it's all connected.*

Meditation comes in many forms, such as walking in nature, being in water, movement, painting, writing, cooking, interacting with animals, and so much more! See, you've been meditating. Carve out some time to explore what meditation looks and feels like for you.

Are you surprised that meditation isn't the cross-legged, seated practice that your mind created? Your unique form of meditation is the thing that leaves you feeling lighter, more peaceful with a renewed sense of clarity.

Like any new habit, your meditation will get stronger the more you practice.Meditation cultivates inner spaciousness—like a vast and infinite sky that gracefully accommodates all the emotions and life situations you are experiencing. It hosts all the thoughts and emotions that you'd rather not feel or experience taking the edge off and bringing you back to a state of ease and grace.

My meditation practice has varied over the years starting with a free phone app that included a ten-minutes-a-day guided meditation (someone talks you through the practice). This evolved into an unguided self-practice in which I set a timer on my phone and sit quietly for that amount of time. You can meditate alone or with others (in-person or virtually). You can go all-out with a 10-day silent meditation retreat with a lot of people seated meditation and focused for more than ten hours a day, or walk through the woods alone in silence for 30 minutes. Here are some suggestions for your meditation practice:

- There's no right or wrong way to meditate. To believe or be attached to the idea of a "perfect" or "correct" practice hinders you from starting! You may be paralyzed at the thought of trying something new because of a desire to do it perfectly. Perfection sucks the joy right out of the benefits of meditation. Perfectionist tendencies will block you from completing anything. I invite you to let go of any thoughts of perfection—your meditation will thank you!
- Meditation is a tool for you—don't worry or compare your meditation practice to the practice of others.
- When thoughts and emotions arise (especially the uncomfortable ones), know that this is natural. The goal isn't to make the thoughts or emotions go away or shut up, but allow them to be there and watch them pass.
- Start with a few minutes each day to bring your focus to your breath and the sensations of your body. Thought doesn't have a way to carry you away if

your attention is on the breath or body. If your mind wanders, gently bring it back to your breath or body.

- Know that the urge to do something else (check your phone, clean, stop your practice) is SUPER common. If you aren't used to this practice, know that this happens to **everyone**. Make the commitment to meditate, and this impulse will ease with practice.

Meditation is a wonderful tool to cultivate intuition and tap into your inner wisdom. Many of my best and most meaningful decisions arrived after a period of meditation.

Here's an example: When I registered for the 10-day silent retreat that practiced Vipassana Meditation, I was both nervous and excited. I decided to sign up for the wait list for a location in Taiwan (although I was in NYC). It would be fun to visit my parents in Taiwan as well as attend the retreat. I asked the Universe to allow a spot to open up if attending the retreat would serve me. A week later, I received an e-mail from the meditation center that a spot had become available and asked to confirm if I would be attending or not.

A rush of emotions came over me! Just as quickly as the excitement appeared, so did fear and doubt. Would being silent for ten days be my undoing? Would the schedule of waking up daily at 4:00 AM be too strenuous for a sleep-loving person like me? What if I was jetlagged? I called on some trusted friends to get their feedback. Most were not supportive or concerned that this was not right for me. I took a pause and quieted my thoughts to arrive at a conclusion.

I sat in the bathtub and meditated on attending the retreat. In the stillness, my inner guidance was able to emerge and pointed me to *Yes*! I would attend the retreat, trusting that all would be well. This was the right choice. The retreat was not easy, but the benefits far outweighed the imagined concerns of others, as well as mine.

I invite you to surrender your fears, doubts, or thoughts of a perfect meditation practice. Say these words out loud before you begin meditating: "Okay, here goes, I'm about to meditate." This is a beautiful form of self-care in which you build your wisdom and allow your body to unclench from all the "doing" you go through each day. Be open to what is and curious to explore what a meditation practice looks and feels like for you. Make use of the abundance of free resources we have available today. See page 254 for meditation resources.

 EASY EXERCISE

Explore Meditation Tools!

1. Carve 30-minutes to one hour and research meditation tools online or check out the Resource Section on page 254.
2. Familiarize yourself with meditations that are guided, unguided, with music, and themed.
3. Tune into your body. What meditations do you gravitate toward? Choose 5 meditations/visualizations to be the starting point for your Woke Bitch Challenge.

WOKE BITCH CHALLENGE

Prepare to get Heavily Meditated

1. Revisit what resonates with you in the Easy Exercise, queue five meditations/visualization from your research.
2. For the next five days, practice each of the meditations.
3. Allow yourself the freedom to repeat the meditations you enjoy. Keep the meditations you enjoy and find others that light you up.

Try this quick meditation for when you don't have a lot of time.

1. Allow yourself to be in a quiet space on a comfortable cushion or chair. Allow yourself to arrive in this present moment.
2. Gently close your eyes, and lightly place your hands on your thighs.
3. Allow your shoulders to drop away from your ears.
4. While your bottom rests on your comfortable seat, visualize your spine straightening—heart over pelvis, head over heart.
5. Without any agenda or force, observe your breath and allow it to be for a few breaths.
6. As you inhale through your nose, bring you awareness to your breath. Feel your breath expand in your belly and move up through your torso.
7. On your exhale, allow the air to flow out through your nose.

8. Do this for three more rounds of breathing in an out with the intention of offering your vessel the high-quality nourishment of oxygen.
9. Let the focus on your breath fall away as you allow your body to breathe.
10. Take a moment to notice how your body feels and any sensations that arise.
11. Let any thought or judgment of your practice drift away as you return to the feelings within your body.
12. When you are ready, very slowly and softly open your eyes.
13. Thank yourself for the practice.

KEY TAKEAWAYS

- Meditation comes in many forms—explore and follow the form that feels best to you.

- A meditation practice strengthens your internal guidance system (*Way* better than scrolling your social media apps. I promise).

- Think of meditation as a practice of un-doing, as opposed to doing.

CHAPTER THIRTEEN

Looking Tight and Feeling Right

(Tools to help maintain wellness and vitality in your body)

When our basic physical needs are met, feeling good isn't very complicated. Recently, I went through a busy cycle of work and social commitments. I didn't eat or sleep enough. When people asked how I was doing, I replied, "I just hope to get enough sleep and eat enough food." *Sounds rough, right?* Sure, it was a bit rough, and it allowed me to understand how valuable it is to eat foods that nourish my body and nurture my body with eight hours of uninterrupted, high-quality sleep.

Do you have the tools to support your body and feel your best? When I am sleep deprived, my outlook on life is grim. It seems as if the other tools that I know such as a meditation or journaling don't resonate because my body is tapped out. A lifestyle that supports us physically is an important piece of our foundation. When you pay attention to what you're eating and the quality of your rest, you'll see an improvement to your quality of life, too. When you're not as busy with work or other commitments, you'll naturally get enough rest, eat the right foods for you, and eat at consistent times. However, when time to yourself is limited and work demands increase, you may become hypersensitive to expending your energy and how you nourish yourself. Sleep is so important that when you don't get it, you could become grumpy, reactive, and even monstrous.

When you feel this way, try to be gentle with yourself and mindful of not letting this monster out of the bag with other people.

Food: I used to pay less attention to how, what, or when I ate or how eating affected wellness. *C'mon, admit it, do you?* As I got busier, I noticed how a healthy and hearty meal made me feel nourished physically and helped me get through days where I had to mentally dig deep such as preparing lesson plans for courses.

Telling you which type of diet is best for you isn't helpful and possibly harmful. You know best what you should and shouldn't eat. However, our bodies are disconnected from our innate ability to regulate our eating, so where do we even begin?

First, a *diet* means the foods and nutrients you choose to nourish your body. Try not to regard *diet* as food or calorie restrictions. I have tried many different foods over the years and have found that a mostly vegan/vegetarian diet works best for me. Other people find that a little bit of meat is helpful.

After a holiday weekend away with friends where we ate a lot of meat, I had a sense of heaviness and discomfort. My BMs (bowel movements) were irregular. When I started eating vegetables and whole grains the main source of my meals, I noticed a drastic difference. When I ate in an aligned way for me, here's what I found:

- A diet with a lot of dark leafy vegetables is wonderful for my metabolism
- Fruits in season uplift my spirit and are a treat (I'm talking about truly enjoying a fruit, not when you

85

are in a rush and pack a banana in your bag for later in the day)

- A mostly plant-based diet with little dairy or meat makes me feel light and energetic.
- When I reduced my intake of meat and dairy products, the heartburn I experienced went away.
- Eating whole foods and avoiding deep-fried or processed foods feels fantastic. Someone could be vegan and eat French fries, vegan ice cream, and pasta all day. It's still vegan, but it lacks nutrition.
- Educate yourself about the foods you eat and observe how you feel after you eat them. The body is wonderful at giving you cues on what allows it to thrive. As an example, I had a sudden craving for sweet and sour fish. I rarely eat this flavor profile. While I devoured the dish, I had indigestion that kept me from sleeping. This was my second time having this dish, so I realized that this combination somehow doesn't work for my body chemistry. I know this is confusing—how can something you crave not serve you? Sometimes, your mind craves something, like a sweet pastry. Your body may not need sugar. Practice distinguishing the difference between a mind craving versus a body craving.

Woke Bitch Trick: Observe your craving for 30 minutes—if it goes away, it was your mind. If it persists, then your body most likely needs some nourishment. What food and how much will best serve you?

- It may sound tedious or daunting to keep experimenting with foods and observing how your body feels, but it will be worth it to develop a keen sense of what nourishes and nurtures your body.
- Lastly, remember that what you eat is for your vessel, and it's your choice. Forget about popular opinion, what others say, feeling guilty or ashamed, and listen to the deep wisdom of your body.
- Whatever diet choices you make, don't be so strict or attach to a concept/identity of being a certain way. That adds its own pressure and stress to your body. There is no need to be hard on yourself, give yourself leeway, and room for flexibility. Eating a vegan diet was my choice, but it's not who I am, and it may or may not work for you.
- If I need to modify what I eat based on how I feel and the circumstances, then I do so with ease and gratitude for the food I eat. This way of eating and honoring my body is *so much* less stressful on the body and much more enjoyable.

Alcohol: When I'm with new people in a social setting, I'm often asked why I don't drink alcohol. The other question I get asked is how I stopped drinking alcohol. After one wild bachelorette party weekend and consuming alcohol, I didn't feel well. The next-day hangover had me sluggish, moody, and overall unwell. Drinking without thought wasn't something I could ignore any longer. I experimented with not consuming alcohol to see how that would affect my overall physical well-being. When observing my physical body and feeling good are a priority, I noticed that alcohol didn't add more fun or joy to my life. It hindered me from feeling full-on happy, energized, and present in my physical being.

There's no formula to stop consuming alcohol but reflect on *why* you drink alcohol and *why* you want to stop. Once you identify how you want to feel and how important that feeling is—you can come back to that intention. Play the role of the observer to alleviate social anxiety about your choice *not* to order an alcoholic drink.

That initial intention is critical and has enormous power when you make aligned choices. For me, this process was not extremely difficult as I kept company that didn't drink either. Even to this day, at a nightclub, dance, or speakeasy with friends ordering a mocktail or club soda with a lime or cherry is easy and fun.

Lastly, take comfort in knowing that going without alcohol isn't as hard as your mind makes it out to be. As you take baby steps each day to support yourself, you'll see that reducing or eliminating alcohol mindfully honors your well-being. Trust and lean on the Universe to be with you!

If you are experiencing symptoms of Alcoholism, please seek professional assistance.

Food hygiene: It's not just the food you eat, but the setting and state of mind when you eat. During my stint as a salesperson at a hotel, lunch was my only break. I worked in a basement sales office and packed homemade Asian meals in Tupperware to heat-up in the cafeteria microwave. Although my meals were healthy, I often had indigestion and felt nervous or anxious during my lunch hour. Looking back, I realized there was no sense of being to enjoy my food nor was I in a supportive setting to do so. When I ate my microwaved lunches, often, I would get pulled away because a client had a question or another manager wanted to talk about work stuff. This meant that I was shoving food down my mouth, didn't get fresh air all day, and wasn't present when eating my food—a recipe for disaster!

Here are my top tips for food hygiene:
- Before you eat, feel into how excited and grateful you are about the food you've prepared or are about to prepare.
- Bless the food: take a moment to close your eyes, take a deep breath, acknowledge the vitality your food is about to give you, and honor where it came from.
- When you eat, chew your food thoroughly and taste the flavors in your mouth. Science has found that chewing your food thoroughly allows your body to make the juices needed to digest the food, which reduces heartburn.
- Practice eating without using your digital devices such as your phone or computer—I know it's tempting, but this habit alone will amp up your appreciation for your food and life!
- Experiment with eating alone at a restaurant without the technology and take in the look of the dishes, ambiance of the space, taste of the flavors, and feel of the service. *This has come to be one of my favorite ways to unwind.*
- Be discerning of the company you keep or the topic of conversation without fear or guilt. I once found myself at my own birthday dinner with immediate family and relatives, and the topic veered from happy birthday—to how old are you? And then, it

spiraled into matchmaking, egg-freezing, and who recently passed away. *I can't make this shit up.* Your mealtime is a time to recharge and enjoy yourself—don't lose sight of this and be brave to make this a priority and set a boundary around mealtime if you need to (See page 118 about setting boundaries).

Sleep, rest, and downtime: When I don't get enough sleep or downtime, I'm not me. Here's what I want to say about sleep—uninterrupted sleep is critical. Recently, I went through a semester where I taught until 3:00AM, but my dogs and the rest of the community woke up around 8:00AM. Although I got help and went back to sleep for eight hours of sleep, I was constantly tired and fatigued. This led me to understand how critical it is to get high-quality, uninterrupted rest. This is the type of sleep where you hit the bed, and aren't carrying your worries and stresses from the day. To help you create an evening ritual to help you sleep, look on page 250.

What is downtime? Downtime is…
- blocks of unstructured time designated for nothing.
- a pause in your day dedicated to you. This is the time to decide what you want to do or not do.
- great for gathering and re-centering yourself, especially when you are overwhelmed. If you find it hard to get downtime—this is a sign that your body needs it. Schedule downtime in your calendar and keep it sacred the way you do a doctor's appointment.
- an essential form of self-care—allow yourself to unplug from your to-do list and recharge.

Lastly, if you feel guilty or embarrassed for needing or taking rest and downtime, let that shit go! When your body needs to linger in bed a minute longer or you need an hour to yourself to disconnect from others and connect within, give it to yourself. **This is your permission slip to 100 percent indulge, commit, and devote yourself to taking the rest you need.** Imagine taking a nap versus looking at your e-mails or feeling guilty about the nap—can you see how this isn't restful? So, here's an invitation to rest your body and feel *good* about taking care of your body that does so much for you!

Body listening day

1. Carve a day to pay attention to one or more areas in this chapter: food, food hygiene, alcohol, and rest.
2. Listen to your body.

Bonus: Record your observations in a journal, notebook, or voice memo.

WOKE BITCH CHALLENGE

Keeping a body alignment log

Start with the Easy Exercise. Every day, log your observations about what you eat, when and how you eat, the alcohol you consume or don't consume, and the rest you get or don't get. Be sure to include how each experiment makes your body feel. Think about the sensations in your body. Continue your experiments for at least ten days. Give yourself bonus points if you do this Woke Bitch Challenge for a month.

 # KEY TAKEAWAYS

- Practices to support your body's alignment can be as simple as ample, high-quality rest and nourishing food.

- Check-in with your body to discover if a tool is working or not

- Take exquisite care of your body to improve mental, emotional, and spiritual well-being.

CHAPTER FOURTEEN

Your Body's Toolbox

Now that we have learned about how supportive food and rest can be, let's dive into some tools, services, and routines to help fine-tune this magical bod of yours. You don't have to do all of these, but choose a few and check them out. Experimentation will help you know what makes your body happy and what doesn't quite fit.

Reiki: Reiki is a Japanese technique for reducing stress and promoting relaxation and healing. The word Reiki is made of two Japanese words—*Rei*, which means "God's Wisdom or the Higher Power" and *Ki*, which is "life force energy." So *Reiki* means "spiritually guided, life-force energy."

It is done by "laying on hands" and is based on the idea that an unseen "life-force energy" flows through each of us. If your "life-force energy" is low, you may get sick or feel stressed. If your energy is high, you'll be more capable of feeling happy and healthy.

A treatment feels like a glowing radiance that flows through and around you, which treats the whole person (body, emotions, mind, and spirit) creating feelings of peace, security, and well-being.

Crystals: Yes, crystals are beautiful to look at and can uplift your body, mind, heart, and soul. There's no need to jump into the deep end and buy every crystal you see. Choose crystals that call to you. Selenite, amethyst, rose quartz, and clear quartz are a good place to begin your crystal exploration. I keep these by my side when I rest or meditate. If you happen to experience discomfort in a particular part of the body, place a crystal, such as the ones above, on that area to see how it makes you feel. While there is no scientific evidence that crystals are energetic healers, they may bring you a sense of peace.

Flower Essences: Flower essences are a form of alternative medicine based on the idea that flowers have a healing vibrational energy. In the 1930s, British physician, Edward Bach thought the energy of flowers could balance our emotions. He believed that this balance could bring mental, physical, and spiritual well-being.

Flower essences and essential oils are often confused with each other. Both solutions are made with plants, but they're prepared in different ways.

There is a lack of scientific research on flower essences, but they are generally considered safe. Like all remedies, there can be unwanted side effects, so check with your health care professional before ingesting flower essences. You can find flower essences at health food stores, herbal pharmacies, and online apothecaries. There are some recommendations on page 256.

Vitamins & Supplements: Natural supplements can be supportive, especially to nurture and care for your body. This is especially true during times of high stress, such as travel or going through life changes—a curated source of supplements to regulate your digestion, sleep, and mood have a grounding effect. You may want to explore a good probiotic, a well-absorbed form of magnesium, vitamin B, zinc, and berbercap supplements. *Check with a health care professional before beginning a health care regimen.*

Essential Oils: Essential oils are often used in aromatherapy, a form of alternative medicine that employs plant extracts to support health and well-being.

Essential oils are compounds extracted from plants. The oils capture the plant's scent and flavor, or "essence." The way the oils are made is important, as some are created through chemical means. Essential oils are not meant to be swallowed or put directly on your skin. The chemicals in essential oils can cause rashes and extreme sensitivity.

Essential oils placed in a diffuser help boost mood and signal the brain to relax. When you smell a relaxing scent, it cues your body to unwind and calm down the nervous system. Select an essential oil scent that appeals to you— after all, these are tools to help your body, and a scent you like can uplift you, too.

Body Oils: Natural body oils applied after a shower or bath in circular motions on your skin not only moisturize but can be wonderful for increasing circulation and blood flow. With better circulation, your body will feel lighter and an inner radiance can emerge. Test different oils on your skin (coconut oil, avocado oil, jojoba oil, olive oil, almond oil, and sesame oil). Some oils are better for different skin types, so do your research. Add a drop or two of your favorite essential oil for an added boost.

Infrared Sauna: Not going to lie—I really enjoy infrared saunas. Sitting in an infrared sauna (not a traditional one) for 30-40 minutes causes *a lot* of sweating. Why do I like it so much? My mind is clearer, my skin is cleaner, my muscles are less achy, and I feel refreshed. Be sure to hydrate before, during, and after your sauna session. Find infrared saunas at health spas and some gyms.

Colonic: A colonic is an infusion of water or other liquids into the rectum by a colon therapist to cleanse and flush the colon. Okay, I know what you're thinking—a tube up the bum, Ew? Colonics with an experienced and licensed practitioner are great. Sure, there were moments of discomfort (especially the first time you try it), but having quarterly colonics has been very healing for my body and overall a comfortable experience. Not only did I let shit go physically—interestingly, it also has a way of unloading mental shit, too. On a physical level, you receive knowledge on what foods don't serve you (the ones you can't digest easily). On a mental level, don't be surprised if you feel a new level of vulnerability followed by newfound courage after a colonic session. There can be serious complications from a colonic, so do your research and consult a health care professional to see if this treatment is right for you.

Celery or Green Juice Cleanse: As a kid, I hated vegetables—especially raw veggies and the super green ones. As an adult, I prefer steamed veggies over raw ones, but super green raw veggies in juice form, yeah baby! If it's your first time enjoying green juices, opt for ones that have some fruit so they aren't as pungent, but don't reach for a sugar-packed green smoothie off the grocery store shelf. Start your day with cold-pressed juices that have more vegetables (such as kale, spinach, and celery) than fruit. They are so refreshing and contain a lot of vitamins to set the tone for your day.

When you have a green juice as part of your day, it boosts your digestion and helps move along that junk food you've been eating. Sure, enjoy caffeinated beverages, but next time, try cold-pressed celery juice to boost your metabolism and detoxify your body. After detoxifying, I have noticed complete bowel movements, increased energy, and clearer skin. *Hey, com'on, you know you care about this stuff.*

Oil-pulling: Oil pulling is an ancient Ayurvedic practice to naturally whiten teeth and remove the gunk and toxins released during sleep. This practice needs to be done first thing in the morning upon waking. First choose a quality oil such as extra-virgin olive oil or coconut oil, and put a tablespoon of it in your mouth and swish it around. Hold the oil in your mouth for 15 to 20 minutes without swallowing it—you'll feel that the consistency of the oil begins to solidify a bit (collecting the toxins). When time is up, spit the oil into your toilet or garbage, but NOT in the sink! It's a great practice to oil-pull as a start to your day—you get silence, stillness, detoxification, and fresh breath and gut! It gets easier with practice. As you begin, hold the oil in your mouth for 1 to 2 minutes and slowly increase the amount of time you hold the oil in your mouth.

Warm water and lemon: This seems like a basic one, but don't dismiss it. You'll notice improved digestion and clear skin when you BEGIN your day with warm water with squeezed lemon. Be sure to select warm water as it is much more soothing to the body than cold or iced water, which can be a shock to the digestive system. If your teeth get sensitive, drink warm water only for a couple of weeks. Then, try the lemon water again.

EASY EXERCISE

Search it

Research one of the tools listed in this chapter and have a casual chat with a practitioner or someone in your circle who has tried one of these tools. Let your curiosity and intuition guide you.

WOKE BITCH CHALLENGE

Book it

Book an appointment or incorporate one of the tools to heal your body.

KEY TAKEAWAYS

- Add tools to your body toolbox to nurture and nourish your body.

- Allow yourself the space and freedom to change, expand, or switch tools as you see fit or as your body's needs change.

- When in doubt or overwhelmed by the tools available to support your body, incorporate them one at a time and start with what is easy for you.

CHAPTER FIFTEEN

Move What Yo Mama Gave Ya

(Movement for Healing!)

Spin. Yoga. Hiit. Cardio. Dance. Weights. Barre. Circuit Training. Lift. Running. Oh My!

The options for today's workouts are endless. I have certainly tried several types over the years and not all of them have stuck around. I am not here to tell you which type of exercise is the most effective and certainly not here to tell you which one is best for you. Just like food, you and your body know best.

There was a time when my mind made up a rule that *I must work out at least 4x a week or else something bad would happen.* I never followed-up with my mind to question what the "or else" would be. The rule of 4x a week and being surrounded by friends in NYC who also worked out 4x a week was enough to somehow make this rule stick. I booked all my workouts and sometimes it was too much for my body to do a certain type of class at the frequency I was going. Whenever I canceled the class, I felt guilty for missing my exercise. The initial intention and natural benefit of feeling good moving my body was lost because I was so hard on myself and *FOMO was real!* Many of my exercise routines were driven by the fear of getting fat, unhealthy, or unfit if I stopped. Movement driven by fear isn't very relaxing or healing, even if I burned a lot of calories or felt sore after a workout.

A few years ago, my body was under a lot of stress and anxiety that had my body feeling numb. I couldn't get out of bed, walk my dog, or workout. It was frightening. This made me listen deeper to what my body needed. It made me reflect on what was right for my body and reset how I moved my body. My body needed gentle movement, so every time my mind made a statement, *"I should run today. I haven't run at all this week,"* I gently asked myself, *"What does my body need right now?"*

Leading my workouts, exercises, and general movement routines with "What does my body need right now?" was a gamechanger. I had more energy, felt more joyful and also more connected with my body. My movements were driven from a place of love and care instead of fear.

Moving the body is a wonderful gift of support for a healthy and joyous life. There are many types of exercise, so try different ones to see what speaks to your body. Here are some things to consider about healing your body through movement:

- Ask your body what type of movement it would like to engage in today. If the body is asking for rest, listen to that, too.
- There is no right or wrong workout—check in with your intentions for exercise and notice if it is coming from a fear-based *"If I don't workout, ___ will happen,"* or a love-based *"I get to workout today,* or *I choose to rest today."*
- When you listen to your body for guidance on how to move, the benefits are far greater. You find yourself smiling during your exercise and even appreciating the challenging moves because you want to be there.

- Don't be attached to any workout. There is no rule saying you have to do the same workout for the rest of your life. Mix it up and have fun. It's natural for your exercise routine to change. Injuries, illness, age, goals, intentions, living situations, and locations that may influence your movement practice. Don't be hard on yourself. Practice welcoming new forms of movement with curiosity, gratitude, and joy.
- Use movement to cultivate presence and compassion. Exercise is the perfect opportunity to practice presence. For example, if you practice a deep stretch, lean into where you feel the stretch in your body, listen to your breath, and observe your mind's commentary about how uncomfortable or difficult the movement is. Moving the body is an excellent opportunity to observe your senses and the narrative in your head. Instead of resisting and trying to tune out, make exercise more fulfilling and effective when you're fully present.

Movement doesn't need to look a particular way or mimic what your friends or neighbors are doing. Below are some suggestions for moving your body. Use the list to inspire you or ask what your body needs. What exercise from the list resonates with your body today?

- Walk, jog, or run
- Biking (outdoors or in a spin studio)
- Yoga (heated, restorative, vinyasa, yin yoga)
- Stretch, Barre, Pilates
- Tai Chi or Martial Arts
- Boxing

- Strength training , Weight lifting, or Circuit training
- Dance Party (Bollywood, Latin, Hip-Hop, African)
- Swimming or Water Aerobics
- Sports (tennis, basketball, baseball, softball, football, volleyball, soccer)
- Pole Dancing
- Skating
- Jumping rope
- Canoing, Kayaking, Rowing, Paddle board
- Gardening
- Rock Climbing or Hiking
- Crossfit
- Skiing or Snowboarding
- Hula Hoop
- Frisbee or Frisbee golf
- Slackline
- Trampoline or Rebounding
- Use a standing desk
- Play with your pet
- Skateboarding
- Surfing
- Cleaning or Tidying

What excites you today?

E² EASY EXERCISE

Shake, Shake, Shake

1. Pick a song that you like and shake yo' body!
2. For the entirety of the song, let your body loosen up as you shake your arms, legs, joints, and neck.
3. Start gently, and let your body guide you.
4. At the end of the track, stand in place, feet planted hip width apart, arms by your side with your palms facing out.
5. Feel the energy coursing through your body and be grateful for the vitality that is always there to support you.

WOKE BITCH CHALLENGE

Intentional Movement is Sensational

This is a two-part challenge involving intention-setting and moving with purpose.

1. Take 3-5 minutes in a quiet place where you can connect within and reflect on what element you'd like to focus on when moving your body. You may prompt yourself with the question, "What does my body need to focus on to thrive? What intention serves my body?" Write your intention on a sticky note or piece of paper, and place it somewhere obvious as you'll come back to this over and over again. (The entryway of your home, refrigerator door, bathroom mirror, or car). With this intention, you'll practice two weeks of moving your body aligned with this intention. You don't have to do the same exercise or workout. Your intention might be to become stronger, so you'll incorporate different types of muscle building exercises, which could include yoga, weights, or circuit training.

2. For the next two weeks, listen to your body, and commit to moving your body aligned with your intention. There is no right or wrong number of times or duration, as this practice is about moving your body out of love as opposed to fear or out of guilt (being out of shape, not good enough, too old). Be open to the physical inspiration that arises and follow it! Hint: If any old thought patterns around how, when, or what you "should" be doing arise, gently acknowledge and return to your intention.

 # KEY TAKEAWAYS

- Movement is essential for our well-being and is a huge mood booster

- Be willing to kick the "should" to the side and move your body with positive intention, as opposed to being fearful of being out of shape.

- Movement helps us banish unkind thoughts and stories through focusing attention back on our body.

CHAPTER SIXTEEN

Self-healing the Body

During Covid-19, my body went through a lot of trauma and stress getting from one airport to another and waking up in a state of panic every day for two weeks. Like an iPhone battery, I was on 10 percent and low battery mode. By the time I got to Taiwan, my battery would be dead. When I reached my destination more than 24 hours later, I took off my clothes to shower and found blisters on sensitive areas of skin that were painful. My body was broken. If you're wincing just reading this, imagine how I felt! It was a total ouch.

The anger, sorrow, and guilt I felt about Coronavirus had my body in a state of panic. Now, my emotions showed up on my body.

The sores brought grief. I was sorry that my poor body was going through this. I had let my vessel down, and Coronavirus won, which affected my mental, physical, and emotional health. Yep, they are all tied together. Why didn't I meditate more? Why didn't I eat better foods or take my supplements? My mind grappled with analysis, blaming and shaming my lifestyle and food choices. I let myself get into a narrative loop of "I should have known better!" My emotions reflected resistance to the present moment, my condition, and being in Taiwan. I didn't like feeling this way and couldn't accept it either.

I reached out to a trusted Reiki healer, who gave me the idea to send my body love by talking to it in a loving and nurturing way. Every morning and evening, I said to myself, *"It's okay, I love you. You'll get better soon."* Eventually, the guilt, sorrow, and anger subsided—a holistic healing took place. The words created a sense of gratitude and awe for my body. Each time I took the meds—I said to the medicine, *"Thank you for helping me heal."*

My story didn't have to be a reminder to blame and shame my body. I was grateful for the access to medication that aided my body in recovering. Michael Beckwith talks about the body temple being an asset and not a liability. Your body isn't an enemy. It's not a parent or caregiver who will berate you for not having done a better job at taking care of it. When you have deep respect and honor for your body, an experience like this can help you understand the truth of your vessel—it will always love and support you no matter what. From this place of unconditional love, say *thank you* to your body and practice treating it with reverence and love.

E² EASY EXERCISE

Profess your love and appreciation for your body

You can practice in front of the mirror or in a space where you feel comfortable. If practicing in front of the mirror, select a full-length mirror so you can gaze on different body parts to be revered.

1. Close your eyes and reflect on your vessel and the experiences it has carried you through. Allow yourself to reflect and revel in how much your body has been through and how strong it is.
2. Allow yourself to reflect on a particular area or experience. Open your eyes and look directly at that area of your body and gaze at your reflection in the mirror.
3. As you gaze at your body, say out loud the gratitude your heart holds for your body. For example, if you had knee surgery, linger on this area a bit longer and say, *"Thank you for being there when I injured myself and allowing me to be active again."*
4. Come back to this Easy Exercise to re-up your appreciation. Feel free to apply it to any area of your body.

WOKE BITCH CHALLENGE

Bless your boo-boo

This Woke Bitch Challenge is most powerful when you happen to have a wound, illness, or injury.

1. Meditate with your boo-boo.
2. Take medicine with ease, thanking its power to heal.
3. Thank the body's ability to heal.
4. If using ointment or cream, lovingly cleanse the wound and apply the ointment with intention, visualizing the Universe's healing power behind it.
5. Observe any uneaseful feelings or thoughts around your hurt or pain and lovingly dissolve it through communicating your gratitude for your body in a loving, nurturing, and Divinely feminine way.
6. Repeat this exercise for as long as your body is healing, and remember to praise your body for the improvements it makes while healing.

KEY TAKEAWAYS

- Your body loves you no matter what.

- Honor your body through professing love and well-wishes to it.

- When you experience any ailment or pain in your body, be curious about the message your body is sending you. Remember, your body it is always guiding you toward your highest good.

- The mind and body can work well together, but please seek medical advice for your hurts and pains.

111

CHAPTER SEVENTEEN

Let that Shit Go!

Here's an unconventional way to be physically, mentally, emotionally, and spiritually healthier—tidying!

Yes, I see you giving me an arched eyebrow wondering if I am turning into Marie Kondo and asking you, "Does this spark joy?" But, tidying up can help you live a more balanced life.

I enjoy shopping, but the issue in the past was that I was never "at home" while being home, especially alone. I was surrounded by a bunch of items and things, but never felt complete or at ease. Are you using shopping as a way to cope with fears, stress, or overwhelm?

Finding things in my closets and drawers was difficult. I often lost things, which caused a lot of frustration. I was a hot mess. Tidying or decluttering your home is healing and sharpens your decision-making skills, and has an impact on your health and well-being.

The tidying process:

Take a full inventory of everything you own and keep only what gives you all-the-good-vibes—this will fine-tune your decision-making skills. When you become sensitive to the things that uplift you and let go of the things that no longer serve, you'll find gratitude for everything you own. This sensitivity and new ability to tune into your joy-radar extends to people, places, and situations, too.

When you embark on your tidying process, you may face some hard truths that may be difficult to swallow. Do you have a pile of designer clothes you've never worn? Are you a stationery or pen hoarder? You may experience a range of emotions such as guilt, shame, or anger.

To clearly look at what you own and make choices about what to keep and what to let go, takes courage and compassion for yourself. Gently tell yourself, *"Hey, I'm not a bad person for having hung onto these things."* Instead focus on the ideal vision you have for your life. If you want to be home and feel at home, or want a space that is a peaceful, safe sanctuary, hold onto your vision and revisit it often. Here's the tidying process in a nutshell:

1. Choose a room, closet, or drawer.
2. Take everything out of the room, closet, or drawer.
3. Clean, sweep, dust, and vacuum the empty room.
4. Go through the room's contents one-by-one and ask yourself:
    *   Is this something I use?
    *   Do I absolutely need this?
    *   Do I love it?
5. Then, put it in one of three piles.
    *   Goes back into the room. *(fits criteria of use/need/love)*
    *   Maybe.
    *   Gets donated or thrown away.
6. Put everything that you're keeping back in the room.
7. Review the "maybe" pile and whether it truly adds value to living your best life. If not, let go with gratitude and move it to the throw away or donate pile.
8. With gratitude, throw away or donate the last pile.

After tidying:

After the tidying process—you'll find space for the things, people, and situations that are meaningful to you.

For added incentive to tidy up, here's a list of the possibilities after you tidy and declutter your spaces.

- Feel more energy to live your life as opposed to wasting energy looking for lost items and feeling scattered and unorganized.
- Experience more confidence in your decision-making skills. You may find that you'll say "yes" with more enthusiasm and "no" with more conviction.
- New passions, interests, and creative flow may arise. For example, you may find that the books left on your bookshelf relate to spirituality or travel. These books can point toward your bliss and passions.
- Your mind becomes sharper and more present. What do I mean by this? Before tidying, most of us are bogged down with attachment to our things through memories or a perceived need someday. When you tidy up for reals, you choose to meet yourself where you are *now* and let go of attachment of the past or future.
- Tidy spaces translate to tidy minds and bodies. After tidying, you may be at ease and look forward to being at home each day. You'll be able to focus on the tasks at hand or to give a loved one undivided attention. On a physical level, you may find that your skin clears up, your digestion improves, and you feel less bloated.

There are so many possibilities that can come from tidying—there is really nothing to lose. Have you noticed within yourself that it's hard to focus on tasks when you are surrounded by clutter? How many times do you get into a clean and throwing away mode when you're procrastinating about something else? Perhaps we surround ourselves with clutter so we don't have to face the truth of who we are.

I take these behaviors as a sign that our souls want us to be physically, mentally, and emotionally well. Tidying our spaces is one tool that helps us get there.

 EASY EXERCISE

Quick clean up!

1. Pick a corner, desk, or small area to tidy.
2. Give yourself 20-minutes on a timer.
3. Notice how the space looks and feels after the quick tidy-up. Keep a journal handy to write your thoughts and emotions.

WOKE BITCH CHALLENGE

Co-create your space

Tidying is a way to co-create with the Universe and get closer to your goals and dreams. This is the ultimate motivation to move forward, especially when it gets tough, messy, and you're overwhelmed by being surrounded by your stuff. Take time to visualize how your life will be at the end of this process. It's super-important! Let yourself dream your dream to supercharge your tidying game.

1. Visualizing your idea lifestyle prompts: How do you want to spend your days? In three words, how do you want to feel inside your home? What does the beginning and end of your day look like? Who do you wish to spend time with?
2. To expand further, you may write out words, sketch, scrapbook or create a Pinterest board with images that reflect your idea lifestyle.
3. Here comes the fun part. Why do you want this lifestyle? Ask why four to five times, especially if your response is along the line of "because I want to be tidy" or "because I am an adult, and my house should be neat."
4. Let your inquiries inspire you to tidy!

KEY TAKEAWAYS

- A cluttered space often reflects a cluttered mind and body.

- Tidying your space can help manifest and welcome new opportunities and possibilities.

- The practice of mindfully decluttering and letting go is a great way to accelerate your decision-making skills.

CHAPTER EIGHTEEN

The Real You
(Authenticity and Boundaries)

For those not used to setting boundaries, they can come across as harsh. Boundaries invoke an image like the "talk to the hand" look. This is definitely *not* what boundaries are about or how to set them. Setting boundaries doesn't have to be stand-offish, mean, harsh, or make another person feel dismissed. Instead, I invite you to look at boundaries as healthy fuel for your authentic self. Boundaries are filled with nourishing, vitamin-packed energy that enables you to go into the world, shine, fulfill your purpose, and be one-hundred percent you. Do you feel a little less intimated by boundaries?

Whenever I complained about work or other life situation in which I felt less than, a therapist, my friends, and family told me to "set boundaries." They meant well, but I had no idea what they were talking about or how to begin. I visualized myself confronting somebody, which made me even more insecure. *You feel me?*

Talking about my purpose, goals, visions, and desire to bring more light to this world is easy and feels good, exciting, and uplifting. When I think of the good stuff, all types of amazing ideas well up inside me. I'm down with creating visions and goals any day, but setting boundaries makes me groan and cringe.

Think about setting boundaries as a gem that holds your inner power. If you magnify this part of you, your boundaries, you'll be able to shine your light a little brighter. *Spoiler: that full-blown confrontation that your mind made up doesn't exist.* If the word "boundaries" gives you discomfort or anxiety, feel free to chuck it or replace the word with "shining your light" or "speaking your truth." This book is intended to help you feel good being you—so you have permission and freedom to modify as you see fit!

I can't possibly write about authenticity and boundaries without sharing about an incident in which I felt my boundaries were crossed and what I did about it. One semester, I was tasked with teaching a course I've taught many times before, but this time it was online instead of in the classroom due to the worldwide pandemic. I was confident in teaching this course. There was a lot of engagement and a lot of students shared how much they enjoyed the course and the way I taught the material. At the beginning of every class, I incorporated a breathing exercise/meditation. In the classroom, I turned down the lights and guided the students to relax their bodies, fully arrive, and let go of anything that happened prior to this moment. Teaching online turned out to be a challenge. I had to shift my approach and set boundaries for the students. In person, I was able to gauge the student's attention. By reading the temperature of the room, I made sure the students behaved. Once the class was online, I lost all sense of control. The meditation experience was much different as everyone became a little muted square on my screen.

Many weeks into the semester, the brief meditation exercise was interrupted by giggling and chatter. During this quiet time, I opened my eyes to one of the students and her friends chatting unmuted, which caused a huge disruption. I was furious. This was the latest in a series of inappropriate behavior in this online classroom. I told the students that class is still class whether it's online or in-person. They had to be in an appropriate place to take the class and let me know if they had trouble accessing the course. In this same week, I had students who didn't turn on their video because they were having bad hair or skin or were taking my class from a public setting such as a shopping mall. I was at my wit's end.

My mind went bonkers. I had trouble sleeping, plagued with thoughts of how the students could be so inappropriate, immature, and disrespectful. Part two of my thoughts circled around how I could get them to change, what type of lecture about behavior I should give, and also berating myself for having been too nice and soft. There didn't appear to be a solution and my anger persisted. I paused to find stillness and meditate for a solution. To me, the behavior was a boundaries violation. Meditation helped me uncover a few things:

- I had to surrender my situation to the Universe and release any action that my mind wanted to take.
- I had to let go of how others behave as offensive and upsetting to my world.
- I had the choice to put up a boundary or not.
- Nothing is worth more to me than my inner peace and freedom.

I realized I didn't want to lose sleep over this disruption. I talked to a trusted colleague who agreed that the behavior was inappropriate and informed me that the University had boundaries set up to back me up as needed.

Talking to my colleague was a blessing, and it also made

120

me realize that somewhere along the line, I had attached my self-worth and emotional well-being to the students' performance. This hindered me from setting healthy boundaries. My ego made the students' behavior a reflection of my ability, which made me feel powerless.

Once my ego wasn't involved (the part of me that wanted to lecture them and say "You know in the real-world..."), I was able to address the students in an authentic and honest way about academic expectations and consequences. The talk wasn't as easy as writing an e-mail, but when I had more clarity, setting a healthy boundary was easier.

After this, a weight was lifted off my shoulders and the flow was back! Call it what you want, but recognizing the value of being and staying authentic and aligned with my values allowed me to pick up with the students without resentment and continue to put my energy and passion into bringing the course alive.

Speaking my truth and surrendering any external need from the students to behave a certain way allowed me to focus on shining my light. I learned that boundary-setting is beyond what I like or dislike, and more about grounding into the guidance that each of us can achieve our best self without fear or interruption. For example, I didn't set boundaries with the students until the students behaved inappropriately. Although I didn't enjoy creating the boundary any more than they liked me having them, the boundaries were necessary for a productive learning environment. Boundary setting wasn't based on my ego, mind, or emotions. To know and learn this lesson helped me move forward with more confidence when I set the next boundary.

Ask yourself, what matters to you? What do you value?

Self-inquiry is really damn enlightening and supportive to our authenticity. The more you practice authenticity and setting boundaries around what you value, the happier you'll be. When you know who you are versus who other people want you to be or who you think you should be, you'll be more open to letting things go and setting boundaries around things that matter to you.

Be mindful of the *"should"* word. I once saw some phrase that was brilliant, woke, and funny. It read, "Don't let others *should* on you and don't *should* on yourself either." The *should* might as well be synonymous to *shit*. When the word *"should"* arises, it points to a place of being **not-okay** with what is and takes you away from the present moment and magnifies all that is wrong instead of everything that is amazing and wonderful. When you step into your authenticity, you are no longer interested in shitting on yourself or shitting on other people. Sounds fantastic, right?

One of the top regrets dying people have is giving so much time and energy pretending to be someone else. Let that sink in a bit—the pull to please others or be seen as "good" or "worthy" is there, but we can choose to return to our true self. In pondering your authenticity—consider these questions. You may want to write about them in your journal.

- What matters to you? What do you value?
- When do you feel most authentically you?
- What allows you to be most authentic?
- Do you feel most authentic alone or with others? If others are involved, who are these people and what traits do they possess?

- What activities do you enthusiastically engage in?
- Which activities do you enjoy so much that you lose track of time?
- What boundaries need to be set around your values?
- How will you set the boundaries that need to be set?

Reflecting on these questions will help you be more confident in your decision-making and help you know where and when to set the boundary around what you value. When you set boundaries, don't worry about pleasing others because when you shine your light, you allow others to do the same!

Examples of what boundaries can look like (it can be more subtle than you think!)

- Put or extend the hours of your phone on DND (to block notifications for calls, messages, app alerts).
- When the situation or conversation feels "off," excuse yourself to the restroom or use the time to take a few conscious breaths.
- Choose to pivot an uncomfortable or toxic conversation in a different direction or express your discomfort out loud.
- Turn down any invitation that doesn't align with who you are and what you value—yup, even if it's from family.
- Allow yourself to rest if you feel tired. Many of us push beyond our limits out of guilt or a sense of obligation.
- When asked a question (whether it's an invitation or inquiry), pause and say you'll think about it and get back to them. This allows you more space and breathing room to make an aligned decision.

Here are some traits of an Energy Vampire:

1. **They aren't accountable.** Most Energy Vampires are charming, but disappear when trouble arises and often blame others. If you're made to feel guilty, you've met an Energy Vampire.
2. **Spare me the drama.** Energy Vampires involve themselves in some kind of catastrophe and fling their drama over others in the hopes that you'll absorb it or fix it.
3. **You can't outdo an Energy Vampire.** They struggle to feel happiness for someone else. Instead, they pull energy from you to feed their emotional needs.
4. **Energy Vampires criticize and bully other people.** The truth is they are insecure. They use bullying to dehumanize and prey on others' emotions. You may feel like you owe them your attention or their attacks are somehow your fault.

What do you do when you've met or know an Energy Vampire? First, acknowledge that the interaction drained your energy. Here are a few suggestions to notice and act. Over time, the added stress of an Energy Vampire can cause anxiety, depression, and more.

1. **Establish boundaries.** Sometimes this is easier said than done. This could include setting up areas of your life that the Energy Vampire is not allowed to enter, avoiding extended events, and limiting interactions.
2. **Reshape your expectations.** You may not be able to connect with them as your emotional release.

- Communicate truthfully from your heart. Leave your ego behind and genuinely tell someone what you feel or what support you need.
- Know what is important to you and give yourself permission to commit to your priorities.
- Revisit any shitty *"should's"* in your current situation and how you can dissolve them.

Energy vampires

An Energy Vampire is someone or something that makes you feel drained or fatigued. Your heart and body tells you that your energetic boundaries have been crossed whether the other individual did it consciously or unconsciously.

Energy vampires, whaaat? They aren't some mythical creature—Energy Vampires can be in your circle at home, work, or school! No, garlic and a cross won't help. Although super-pungent, garlic breath may do the trick.

If you are a sensitive individual who has a tendency to be empathetic and deep, you may be called an empath. While it's great to be there for friends and family, sometimes you may feel things so strongly that other peoples' highs can be your highs (yay!), and so can their lows (not so yay). To sustain your health and vitality that allows your light to shine, you'll need to be aware of what and who drains your energy or crosses your energetic boundaries. What do Energy Vampires look like? Unfortunately, it's not as easy to spot Count Dracula in real life, but fortunately your body knows when you've spent time around one.

3. **Cut the cord.** In some cases, you may need to cut ties altogether. You have the freedom to cut this person out of your life entirely. This may feel like drama, too, but you are protecting yourself. Call on the Archangel Michael (a very strong and powerful angel with a big, badass sword) to help you cut the cords with this person and clear your aura of any low vibrations.

4. **Pause, breathe, and visualize a white light** entering the top of your head and exiting your toes removing any toxicity. After clearing anything that doesn't serve, think loving thoughts or do something loving for yourself. Try a bath, make tea, or talk to a trusted friend.

5. **Make a mental note** about your interaction with the Energy Vampire. How did the interaction not feel good to you? Now, reflect on your next steps, if any. There are no right or wrong answers.

6. **Develop self-trust and inner-knowing** that you'll continue to be yourself, set boundaries, and shine your light that no one can dim. Believe that the power and strength you need to deal with any Energy Vampires is within you.

Once, I asked my mom why people with these tendencies seemed to be drawn to me and why they appeared to want my attention, vent, but not want to change their ways so they can help themselves. My mom as usual, graciously replied, "Well, maybe they see your light and want to have that light too, but don't know how." This shows how important your light is (so take good care of it) and also to have compassion for every human being you come across.

126

Here's an analogy to help you cement just how powerful and important you are: would you allow anyone to come into your home and trash it? *No?* Why would you allow anyone to do that to your mind, body, and heart space?

When we begin to look at our energy (mental and physical) and light as a sacred space, we want to keep it pristine like how we want our home to be tidy, cozy, and make us feel good. If someone threw garbage in your home, you would probably ask them to leave and most likely NOT invite them over again. So my friends, let any guilt or doubt melt away. The way you counteract darkness is to keep shining your light, not by dimming your light and joining the darkness.

E^2 EASY EXERCISE

Energy Vampire Bust

Reflect on a recent encounter with someone in your life who may be an Energy Vampire (EV). How did the interaction drain your energy? What is a loving and constructive way to preserve your energy? Having reflected on the action to alleviate the situation, make a note in your journal about how to act next time you encounter an EV.

WOKE BITCH CHALLENGE

Pledge to Authenticity

After you feel one of your boundaries being crossed, pledge not to push away those who cross your boundaries, but instead commit to your values, and let your values lead you to next steps. Write a pledge to your authenticity and commit to YOU.

1. Find yourself in a space you feel comfortable and access your inner guides. In your journal or a piece of paper, jot down any words or phrases that come forth when you ask your inner guide, "What matters to me?" Focus on letting your words flow in an unrestricted way. If you get stuck, feel free to use your memory to recall a situation in which

you felt amazing or the thought, "this is what I am supposed to be doing" crossed your mind. Include your memory as part of your writing. Allow yourself to welcome the elements of this memory that contributed to you feeling this way.

2. Pause upon the completion of your writing and take a deep breath with your eyes closed.

3. Open your eyes and read what you wrote. If you want to linger in the delightful surprises, allow yourself to do so.

4. Create your pledge, and make it personal to you. This isn't a homework assignment you'll share with the rest of the class. So you won't find a template here (sorry, not sorry). To get started, adopt the following as part of your pledge if you'd like.

_____ *matter to me.*

I feel best and most myself when I _____, _____, *and* _____.

Doing _____ *speaks to my true self.*

(People, places, or things) align me with who I am.

As a pledge to myself, my purpose, and authenticity, I remind myself I am _____.

In the face of a challenge, I will _____.

I love myself and I am my best being _____.

The boundaries I need to set are around _____.

5. Autograph your pledge, baby!

KEY TAKEAWAYS

- Exercise and set healthy boundaries as a form of self-love.

- Believe and know that your authentic self deserves to be seen and respected.

- Tools such as prayer and speaking your truth can keep Energy Vampires at bay (and you feeling free).

YOUR BODY IS THE MOST IMPORTANT VESSEL IN THE WORLD.

PART 3
The Heart (and Emotions)

Emotions and feelings often start with thoughts and aren't separate from the thoughts. Every emotion is your body and heart's reaction to a thought or outside stimuli. When you develop a sense of awareness, you'll see how emotions show up and which thoughts were attached to that emotion.

MAKE YOUR HEARTSPACE THE SPA SPACE OF YOUR DREAMS

Note: *If you are having suicidal thoughts or are experiencing depression, please seek professional psychological advice. Sometimes our thoughts and emotions need the support of professionals to help us feel well again.*

CHAPTER NINETEEN

A Jab to the Heart!

(and other emotions that get stuck in the body)

Ever noticed that you can't bypass an uncomfortable emotion by pretending you're okay or denying that the emotion exists in the first place? Imagine you have a thought that is bothering you. You sense it manifesting in your body as an emotion. Good for you for being aware!

As you go about your day, you meet people here and there that give you a chill *"Wassup?"* You respond *"I'm fine."* Oops! You may be masking the true emotion that is coursing through your veins. It's like your emotions are so consuming, energetically stored or stuck in your body. Hey, it's not easy sharing emotions because we've all been taught to guard how we feel. When we tell someone close about our emotions, sometimes we even feel like a burden. Yikes!

Someone once shared in a joking manner that "fine" actually stands for fucked up, insecure, neurotic, and emotional. When you hide your emotions, it may seem appropriate not to spill your guts to everyone you meet. A simple *"I'm stressed right now"* could be perfect.

When emotions aren't released, they often get stuck in the body as excess energy, which can later manifest as stress or illness. This excess energy is like stepping on gum, and it's still stuck on your shoe (*a nice new pair of shoes*). The emotion eats at you and annoys you the entire day. Sometimes emotions can be sneaky and sticky after you've removed the gum from your shoe. You can't tell the emotion was ever there, but the mind and emotions work together to form new thoughts: *"I can't believe this happened to me. I just ordered these shoes."* The gum is long gone, but the emotions hang around all day helping the mind come up with new thoughts, which stress the body. It's a vicious cycle.

This is why the inner landscape of your heartspace and emotional body is so damn important. You want to keep it pristine and beautiful, like the spa space of your dreams. Without awareness, emotions hang on for dear life and turn your gorgeous spa space into a gum-chewed alley.

I know we probably want to raise our finger and go "damn you, emotions," but emotions aren't the problem. Emotions are an automatic response influenced by our evolutionary and personal past experiences to deal with a current situation or thought.

There are ten types of basic emotions, as described by psychologist, Paul Eckman:

Happiness
Sadness
Disgust
Fear
Surprise
Anger
Pride
Shame
Embarrassment
Excitement

These emotions can combine to form secondary or complex emotions. For instance, joy and trust can combine to create love. You can see how this can get confusing.

We express our emotions through facial expressions, body language, and tone of voice. It's difficult to hide your emotions completely. The realities of what contributes to an emotion is complex and based on the individual.

Eliminating emotions isn't possible, but you can make peace with your emotions and allow them to naturally flow through you as you come back to the present moment.

E² EASY EXERCISE

Chain Reaction

One way emotions (buried and apparent) find a way to communicate is through your body's emotions.

In this EE, explore the connection between your emotions and body.

1. Make a loop with your thumb and index finger on both hands, loop them together to make a chain.
2. While keeping the tips of your thumb and index finger tight, say a true statement such as "My name is ____." And pull your hands apart while keeping the chain tight. Observe how you feel.
3. Experiment with another statement, repeat the line above but replace your name with a false name.
4. Are your muscles strong with the true statement or the false statement?
5. Explore the connection between your body and the emotions in your body. Apply this to other statements to understand how you feel. In many cases, a statement that feels true will result in your muscles holding the chain together and statements that don't align with your truth allows you to break the chain.

Have fun!

WOKE BITCH CHALLENGE

Soul retreat for your emotions

This Woke Bitch Challenge is about maintaining your heart space, watching how your thoughts affect your emotions, your emotions affect your body, and being compassionate with yourself when emotions occur. *Hint: If you are berating yourself for your emotions, then Judge Ego has arrived.*

1. Sit quietly and allow a thought to rise in your mind and the emotion to flow.
2. Then, look at your face in a mirror. What do you see?
3. Now, go out into the world and watch others. When someone says, "I'm fine" check their body language, facial expressions, and tone of voice. What do you see?
4. Being aware of others' emotions is a great way to become aware of your own.
5. Now, when your next emotion rises to the surface to be seen, cultivate your heart space with kindness, comfort, and gentleness. Say something to yourself that you would tell a dear friend or family member, if they were experiencing this type of emotion.

KEY TAKEAWAYS

- One kind of healing practice is giving your emotions space.

- Stuck emotions can manifest in other areas of your body and life.

- Your heartspace is your inner temple for all the feels of being human (and let's keep it tidy and pristine).

CHAPTER TWENTY

Ghosting Your Emotions Doesn't Work

I once read that you can close your eyes to what you don't want to see, but you can't close your heart to what you don't want to feel. What does this mean?

If we suppress difficult feelings, they still exist. Bypassing emotions and pretending they don't exist is a form of suppression, which blocks healing and feeling good.

One late summer a few years ago, I full-on committed to a jet-setting corporate role in sales for the world's largest hospitality company. I enjoyed the job for a long time and remember feeling like this was what I "did." You know what I'm talking about—when you're so committed to a job, home life, or hobbies that no one can comment on it being "just a job" or expressing concerns about you being too tired. I wouldn't hear any of it, and thought, this is who I am, and this is what I do.

I welcomed any opportunity to take my hospitality career to new heights, including teaching hospitality courses at my alma-mater. I enjoyed teaching so much that I wished for more teaching opportunities. Of course, I kept performing at a high level at my full-time sales role, too. At this point in my life, meditation and well-being were not part of my days. My idea of well-being was getting a massage, working out, and getting my nails done. Life has a funny way of showing you what you need to learn and where you need to grow. I was an expert, so staying busy and my own self-worth was caught up in "doing it all." I had it all—an enviable career, dedicated family, and found time to stay fit and teach. There was no inner practice or self-care but a hell-a-lot to look at or read on my resume.

One summer, I was assaulted at a social event, which traumatized me. Physically, I was *A-okay*, so life would resume as planned. Then, life kicked me in the stomach. The day after the assault, I had an argument with my partner and couldn't move from my bed. No, my bones weren't broken, but mentally, physically, and emotionally, I was paralyzed. My entire body was numb and electricity coursed through my body, which imploded. I was a shell of my former self. My soul hung over my physical form and observed the husk of me lying on the bed. Things weren't right, and yet, I pretended that I would bounce back as I did before. There was a wound on the surface, but my mind continued with old patterns of thought. I called out sick with a fever. This intense feeling of implosion with a shell of nothingness continued for three days. I couldn't eat, sleep, talk to anyone, or walk my dog. Life as I knew it had ended in dramatic fashion, and I didn't even have on-point nails to show for it.

Some people labeled what happened as a panic attack. The experience was an accumulation of patterns, habits, emotions, and life pressures that I didn't allow to come to the surface.

Imagine you're a human garbage truck. Deadlines, sales targets, arguments in the relationship, frustrations, and all types of life stressors happen. Each time these experiences reach a threshold, the energetic and emotional being presses the difficult emotions down with force and compacts them into a heavy-duty, big-ass garbage truck. The waste "disappears" in the back with a big crush. People throw more garbage in the back, and the truck and its mechanisms go CRRSSSHHHHH in a deafening way. Then, *voila*—out of sight, out of mind. So I can say I was a capable, wrap dress wearing, emotional garbage truck—*my cool and even-keeled persona was proof, right?*

Here's the tricky part—garbage doesn't disappear in the truck—your emotional garbage, stress, and life pressure don't go away either. Do you know the emotional garbage you're carrying around? Do you need to empty your garbage truck and maintain it a little better?

When I was paralyzed in bed, I realized that my internal garbage truck fell in on itself because of the emotional weight I was carrying. The mechanisms that I put in place— gettin' my hair and nails done and the occasional massage— weren't helping me perform my best. They were keeping up appearances, as the garbage got compacted deeper and deeper where I didn't have to see it. For the first time, I saw what I had been doing and my Being had enough. My heart and soul whispered to me over the years asking me to pause, take a break, or tend to my vessel. This physical barrage finally got my attention. I had a **complete** knowing that I must tend to myself and a few sick days would be futile. If you've had an experience like this or you're cringing, I feel ya. It was painful and strange, but it *woke* this bitch *up*.

*Note: If you are experiencing the effects of trauma, please seek professional support.

Imagine making a collage of who you are—include childhood pics, degrees, words, roles, and images of your hobbies, family, and friends. You've been working on this collage *forever*! Year after year, you add to the collage, new people you meet and experiences you have. If someone asked, *"Who are you?"* You would pull out your curated collage and proudly show the person who asked. You forget it's a collage—you're dedicated to crafting the images—the collage has become who you are.

If you have an emotional implosion, it is as if the Universe or your Higher Self blows up your valuable AF collage. Salvaging the bits was useless—it is beyond repair. Your true self, the one emptied of the emotional garbage must emerge and leave the collage behind.

This is what I learned:

- Tend to your inner garbage regularly and allow yourself the ease of letting the emotions come out and release.
- Suppressing your emotions isn't the same as working through or feeling your emotions. To feel your emotions and spend time in introspection promotes healing.
- Emotional suppression will result in implosion or explosion.
- Recognize the grace given of Universe when an experience appears to be unpleasant, such as physical ailment, emotional anxiety, or panic.
- Realize that emotions are *all* okay. Emotions can *all* be present at the same time—rage, joy, anger, jealousy, grief, shame. Your Higher Self knows that the emotions are not who you are. They are felt sensations in the body.

144

- The first step to releasing the compacted emotional garbage is to allow space for these emotions to exist. They are all valid.
- Asking or wondering when all the discomfort of emotions will go away only helps it stick around. The more you allow your emotions to just "be" without taking action, the sooner they will move through you and dissolve.

EASY EXERCISE

Garbage check-in

Is there anything I want to acknowledge and release right now?

With the question above, notice what comes up for you. Try not to judge or justify what emotions show up and go with whatever your heart has identified as garbage. Say out loud or in your heart, "thank you for surfacing, and I discard you now."

Tend to your inner garbage regularly and allow yourself the ease of letting emotions come out and letting them go.

WOKE BITCH CHALLENGE

Compassion for your feelings

This WBC is about cultivating compassion for the difficult emotions in your life—the ones that create a hot mess.

Practice allowing what is happening in your emotional body, perhaps whisper, *"This belongs."*

Try it and watch what happens to yourself energetically and emotionally. Do you feel more spacious? Allow yourself to experiment with this WBC for eleven days.

 # KEY TAKEAWAYS

- Suppression of emotions isn't the same as working through or feeling your emotions. To feel through your emotions and spend time in introspection promotes healing.

- Just because you feel broken doesn't mean you are broken. The soul is unbreakable.

- The Being who heals you is *you*. You are the light at the end of the tunnel!

CHAPTER TWENTY-ONE

Subbing Your Feelings with Substance

My path to not consuming alcohol came about naturally and has been this way for more than two years. When I met some new friends, the topic of alcohol came up. They were surprised to learn I don't drink. They asked a simple, "Why?" I paused and reflected for a second.

As I began meditating and strengthening my awareness, I was more attuned with my body, mind, and spirit. I was also curious about my reactions to alcohol and how this substance affected others. What I found in my experience and observing others, is that substances (drugs and alcohol), temporarily offer relief or a feeling of euphoria (high). Under the influence of substances, the anxious thoughts seem to melt away and you don't "have" to feel what you don't want to because you've been numbed by the substance. For some, drinking alcohol or taking drugs is an escape from the busy mind. Whenever I was in an uncomfortable social situation, such as being around new people or big gatherings, I'd have the urge to drink. The act of drinking alcohol loosened me up and alleviated the perceived discomfort. When it was masked by alcohol, the situation appeared to be easier to navigate. My unconscious mind associated my discomfort and awkwardness with not being good enough. Instead of these thoughts, the buzz and drunkenness got me back into my body, but not exactly in a healthy way. Ya feel me?

Inevitably, I noticed that a night of alcohol fun would result the a following day filled with amplified anxiety, moodiness, and exhaustion. Ugh! For example, if I was anxious the evening before at a level five and I grabbed a drink, the next day, my anxiety rose to a level eight or nine. This can be confusing since the alcohol or substance produces an extreme high and the next day is so low.

Suppression and escaping with substances such as drugs and alcohol didn't work for me. In an attempt to not feel, the feelings came back even stronger than before. Spiritual teacher Kim Eng once shared **that the only way out is through**. To heal the anxiety—the remedy is not escaping it, but opening your heart with courage.

The feeling of anxiety can feel like a punch in the gut or a lump in your throat. Grief can feel like a numbing sensation in your body or a depletion of vitality—your limbs can feel heavy. These sensations sound unpleasant. I invite you to have the courage to feel through the sensations that arise in your body and observe. Watch how your body or mind react to experiencing these sensations and instructing you to have a drink or take a substance. Sensations come and go and with each moment that you choose to feel through the feelings, you are taking steps to heal the emotion that you spent a lot of time and energy to avoid.

Over-numbing SOS:

So you notice your mind is uncomfortable with the current wave of emotions, and it wants you to reach for the drink or substance.

What can you do?

- Thank yourself for having the awareness to notice how you feel.
- Say "this belongs" to the emotion that is currently stirred up and notice how you feel. Whatever you feel belongs, and there isn't anything wrong with you.
- Say "Yes" to the emotion, welcome and feel it, even if it's uncomfortable. Keep opening up to invite more space for the discomfort to dissolve. If it does not dissolve, please seek professional psychological advice.
- Explore and get curious as to where this emotion hits you in the body. Without judgment, watch the sensation arise and dissolve within your body.
- Reflect on your knowing that when you feel through these emotions and sensations, you are taking active steps to heal yourself.
- Make a conscious choice to partake of the alcohol or substance. It is not the outside influences that are affecting your choice. *You* are making the choice.

Note: If you are experiencing substance abuse issues, please seek professional assistance and advice.

E² EASY EXERCISE

Numbing Check-in

Quick journal jot answering "What are some ways I numb my feelings?" *Hint: it doesn't have to involve ingesting anything.* For example, you may insert jokes, change the topic, go shopping, or walk away. These are some ways that we numb or ignore our feelings.

WOKE BITCH CHALLENGE

A Healthy "What-if"

This WBC is about being curious how you would feel omitting a particular substance that is holding you back. Would happy hour be happy without alcohol? This is your opportunity to open yourself to the possibilities.

Ask yourself:
   "What if I didn't do ____ and chose to do ____ instead."

You set the duration, choose the object, and have fun with it. If you have followed your curiosity to try different substances or alcohol, let this be a chance to explore what it's like without those substances.

KEY TAKEAWAYS

- Suppression of feelings with substances such as drugs or alcohol often exacerbate the undesirable feelings you pushed away.

- Cultivating space for your emotions to come up is a healthy practice for healing (and no hangover).

- Regular practices of cultivating your wokeness such as meditation can strengthen the habit of abstaining from drugs and alcohol.

- Substance abuse and alcoholism are a serious health conditions. Please seek professional medical and psychological advice.

CHAPTER TWENTY-TWO

Kicking Fear in the Rear

(and doing it in fab shoes)

One of the most helpful pieces of advice for your spiritual growth is to recognize the voice of fear and choose not to follow it. The voice of fear is super-distinct. It is a character who lives in your mind and talks at you over and over, louder and louder.

The voice of fear carries you away from the present moment. If you notice narratives or hypothetically dangerous situations that might happen in the future or something in the past that you are afraid will repeat itself—that's fear raising its ugly head.

When you are about to enter uncharted territory (even if it's good thing!), the voice of fear has a tendency to plant doubt in your mind. Instead of being upset, recognize the signs and be glad that you are on the precipice of growth.

Fear keeps you in the status quo—it rejects change of any kind, even if that change is positive. Such a downer, right?"

The goal isn't to make fear's voice STFU because resisting or denying that voice only makes it louder. Instead, face the voice of fear head-on and don't let it drive your actions, intentions, or life choices.

Author Elizabeth Gilbert once pointed out that after a while, the fear narrative gets boring. It repeats points that lead to "no" and "stop." When we realize that fear is taking hold, we'll see 101 ways the voice of fear wants you to stop moving forward, taking risks, or trying new things

Even in the process of writing this book or teaching my courses at university—fear has visited me time and time again with *what-if* scenarios. Sometimes the what-if scenarios are so vivid and believable that I forget they're not real. In these situations, pause and ask yourself, would you be happier and more joyful if you didn't do "the thing?" This one question may give you the answers you need to fight fear.

Collective fear can have a big impact on you, too. This is fear felt by your family, circle of friends, your local or the global community. During times like this, it's really helpful to recognize that it's okay to feel fear. Also remember that this is an opportunity to face fear and contribute to the upliftment of the collective or global community.

The practice of surrender, acceptance, and cultivating compassion toward yourself can be a good antidote to fear-based narratives.

Fear is usually tied to other emotions through thoughts and body sensations, such as shame, guilt, sadness, rejection, abandonment, and anxiety.

Here's the sticky part: fear-based stories (your thoughts and misbeliefs) can affect others. Sometimes these false narratives take on a life of their own, spreading like wildfire. Love has the same power with a more positive outcome. When we move our intention back to love and recognize that fear is a shared human condition, we can build compassion and empathy with and for one another. Let love guide your actions, speech, and intentions to be a powerful source of healing for all.

E² EASY EXERCISE

Sup, Fear?

Call out your fear, and then, say: *Wassup*. Do you experience paralyzing fear that stops you from doing what you really want to do?

1. Acknowledge when fear has showed up.
2. Notice the ways in which fear's narrative tries to stop you.
3. Say *wassup* to your fear, and carry on with what is aligned with who you are.
4. Periodically nod to your fear and acknowledge its presence.

WOKE BITCH CHALLENGE

Fear vs. Love

Take an inventory of your fear and love notes. Examine the areas of work, relationships, family, purpose, rest, and wellness (physical, mental, emotional, and spiritual). Is it driven by F or L?

- List and empty out your current Top Five fears, worries, or concerns.
- Review the list and ask yourself if this fear, concern, or worry is derived from love or fear. For example, are you losing sleep over the results of a final exam? Is this concern coming from a loving or fearful place? I'll bet some coin it's coming from fear.
- After you review your list and look at it from a Fear or Love POV, allow yourself to be okay with the discomfort of fear. Imagine a glowing white light of the Love shining over and dissolving your fear. Think of Love like sunlight, a natural disinfectant.
- Now that you are mindful of your fears, practice choosing Love again and again—especially in the presence of fear.

KEY TAKEAWAYS

- After experiencing or feeling fear, growth and positive change often happen.

- Surrender, acceptance, and self-compassion are good antidotes to fear.

- Be kind and recognize that fear is part of being human—don't fear the fear!

CHAPTER TWENTY-THREE

A Spoonful of Sugar Helps the Emotions Go Down

(and other tools to work with the hard-to-swallow feelings)

The other day, I was drowning in intense emotions. Yeah, it still happens from time-to-time. It was almost as if the Universe was like "ha, you want to write about working through uncomfortable emotions? Here's some content for you!" Honestly, it was challenging with a capital "C," and the grip was strong. I'm sure you can relate. It's like getting stuck in quicksand. For me, this particular fear sand was mucky and made up of overwhelm, vulnerability, insecurity, and uncertainty. It was sticky and icky, but I survived. Now, I have a better understanding of how to heal.

When strong emotions seem to come out of nowhere, the mind's first reaction is "Eeew, I don't like this feeling. Get me out of here!" The more you try to get out of the strong emotion, the more intense it may get. Now, your attention is focused on the strong emotion.

Studies have found that an emotion lasts about 90 seconds if you allow it to be present, and don't try to change or resist it. When you are experiencing a challenging emotion with intensity, it may feel like it lasts for an eternity. If you practice acceptance and self-compassion, the emotion passes faster and with more ease.

What you resist will persist.

When you are experiencing a challenging emotion, mental energy of "I don't want this. Make this go away now!" or "What's wrong with me for feeling this way" are all thought forms that keep the emotion stuck front and center in your thoughts. Focusing your energy on wanting the emotion to be different fixes the emotion in place. When you judge yourself with "What's wrong with me for feeling this way"—it actually exacerbates the emotion because at this point, you have already identified the emotion with being who you are. When you judge yourself for having the strong emotion, the thoughts charge the emotion even more. You have identified the emotion as who you are. *Damn!*

On page 24, we talked about thoughts are not who you are—emotions are the same. The story or thought of having to "fix" how you feel is an illusion of the mind tricking you into thinking that you are your emotions, or there is something wrong with feeling the way you do that needs fixing ASAP.

Be the observer. When you're in the grip of emotion—practice being the observer. Instead of thinking, "I am feeling insecure, therefore I am an insecure person," visualize yourself leaning back and watching yourself from a distance feeling these emotions. The person who has stepped back and is observing is who you are. *You* are the witness of what you think and feel. *You* are the awareness of the emotions that stir and tug at your heart. How can this be true? Because you are aware when you feel something uncomfortable and are aware of how your mind tries to fix it. The simple fact that you observe (insert unpleasant emotion), means that you aren't (insert unpleasant emotions). If you are (chosen unpleasant emotion), then there would be no awareness of witnessing of that which you supposedly are. The same is true of pleasant emotions. No playing favorites. Don't believe me? Are you aware when you feel anxious?

Honor the emotion as part of your leveling up. Emotions that arise, especially the challenging ones, are spiritually upleveling—your expansion or evolution. My cousin once said that "God doesn't give us anything we can't handle." It's along the same lines as "What doesn't kill you makes you stronger."

When you think of the phrase "level up," it's most commonly used in a computer or video game where you advance to the next level. Whether playing video games are a distant memory or something you do often—you may notice that it takes several tries before conquering the level at hand. With practice, you'll conquer this level and advance to the next one. Now imagine leveling up spiritually and within your heart the same way. Perhaps, you get triggered emotionally whenever someone makes a comment about your diet. It tugs at your heart and make you feel a little hot and irritated inside. You may even carry these emotions around for days. However, through practice of acceptance and being the observer, you are no longer affected by peoples' comments about this topic, and it's not the last time you'll experience difficult emotions. Next, you may experience some deep-rooted emotions such as fear of rejection or fear of abandonment that have been buried since childhood. It may sound overwhelming, but recognize that you have evolved and moved from feeling irritation to being ready to face deeper and more intense emotions. Know that you *are* ready to work through this, but please don't place a timeline or expectation on yourself. This is another thought and not who you are.

One way to create distance from the intensity of an

emotion is to notice your surroundings. Be in your body. Feel your hands, keep your ears open to the sounds you hear, and notice the sensations you feel in your body. During the emotional quicksand incident, I could feel tingling in my hands and hear the clock ticking in my room—I was able to detach from the grip of the emotions. Coming back to the present moment and into your body through noticing your surroundings is a great tool to turn the focus away from the intense emotions and come back to the physical reality of what is.

Appreciate the music—don't skip the track. Michael Singer likens the feelings and emotions that the heart experiences as *music of the heart*. You may have noticed that the heart experiences ALL types of music of all different genres. Sometimes, it's like a summer pop song, while other times your emotions may feel like the instrumentals in a suspense movie. Be aware that the heart is meant to experience music of all types. Let the music flow through your heart while not skipping the track.

I lost my dog and found her after 32 hours. My heart was all over the place with emotions. If this experience had a movie soundtrack, it would have been a wide range of music from slow to fast, deep or high. Although it was painful to experience the emotions of sadness, grief, and anxiety—the beauty of the joy, delight, and protection when I found her was miraculous.

I encourage you to feel into your heart and let your emotions emote—it is what our hearts are meant to do. We are meant to allow the music to flow through our hearts, without judgment or resistance and with self-compassion and trust.

E² EASY EXERCISE

I've got my eyes on you
(For 90 seconds)

Don't listen to the stats on emotions—put it to the test. Next time you are gripped by strong emotions, watch and observe them for 90 seconds. Notice the change in intensity. What the heck, put a timer to the emotion if you want!

WOKE BITCH CHALLENGE

D-I-Y spell

Come up with your own keyword to prompt a release of emotions. Think Harry Potter's prompts for his wand. I got my magic wand, and I'm gonna use it. This Woke Bitch Challenge puts your magic words into practice for 11 days (Wand and hand gestures welcomed but optional). Here are some examples you may use if you'd like.

- I release you!
- I let this shit go!
- It's just an emotion—it will pass!
- I'm human, no big deal!

KEY TAKEAWAYS

- Studies have found that an emotions lasts for 90 seconds (you can ride this out!)

- Focusing on an emotion you don't want, keeps it energetically stuck.

- You aren't what you think. You aren't what you feel!

CHAPTER TWENTY-FOUR

Speak Your Truth

You know when you're scared to express yourself because you're afraid of hurting others, being judged, or rejected? I've been there. You might be living in a state of suppressing your truth—especially the personal stuff. In my career and in public, I was a master at networking, communicating, and appearing overall confident and articulate.

Expression of how I felt inside was one of the hardest things for me to do. There was so much fear that if I spoke my truth all hell would break loose. One time, when I was struggling to tell someone that I was hurt by something he had done, I reached out to my Reiki healer for guidance. The healer encouraged me to trust that my feelings were true, and to speak to this person from a place of love and knowing my truth.

What is speaking from a place of love? It is when you speak without sarcasm, blame, shame, criticism, and ego. When conversations turn into attacks, you are not speaking from a place of love.

Speaking from a place of love and truth is an expression of the one doing the talking, an invitation for connection, understanding, and vulnerability. A few years ago, I experienced pain from a situation that had gone from innocent chatter to verbal abuse. I kept it from my mom because I was afraid that if she knew, she would freak out or be worried. While my mom was visiting, I found it difficult to be around her and withhold this truth. So, one day, I mustered the courage to share what I had gone through. Mom advised me how to deal with it and "kick it in the butt." It aligned with her tendency to toughen up and move on when shitty things happened. I gently told her from my heart that I wanted to share with her because I love her but nothing needed to be fixed. I also articulated that I wanted her to hold me and tell me everything would be okay. This was a huge step to sharing my truth and expressing what I needed.

Here's a super critical and transformational question that you can ask when a loved one is facing a challenge.

"How can I support you?"

After I experienced a traumatic situation, my cousin asked me this life-changing question: "How can I support you?" I was deep in pain and still wrapping my head around what happened. By her asking this heart-opening question, I went from a spinning mind and hurting heart to instant peace. It served as a catalyst to start my healing by thinking about my needs.

A simple question of "How can I support you?" is an opening for the other person to share what they need and not what YOU think they need. After challenging experiences, we are often told what to do or how to do it. Our mind gets into "troubleshooting" mode, which adds unnecessary pressure.

Have you ever told a loved one about something painful, and they start bitching/trash-talking to alleviate your pain?

Did it help or make you feel better?

By asking an open-ended question, we allow the other person to share their needs and get into the practice of articulating our needs. This isn't easy! It can feel vulnerable and raw AF to express what you need. You may be afraid of the consequences or being judged. However, expressing your needs and truth gets easier and helps everyone involved. At the end of the day, there is an exchange of compassion and support from a place of love and truth with very little guesswork. And that's amazing!

Speaking your truth with Love

In the next week, tune into your love and truth vibration and intentionally choose to have one interaction where you speak from this sacred and powerful place. It may be helpful to consult your calendar and look at your upcoming appointments to identify who you'll speak to. This isn't a speech, so please don't get on your soapbox. This doesn't have to be a negative or difficult conversation. Having a coffee chat with your mentor? Don't hesitate to speak truthfully and lovingly about how they have helped you and how grateful you are. This Easy Exercise is a practice of turning inward, so be on the lookout for your mind wanting to label upcoming conversations as "good" or "bad." Labeling is a sign post that you are steering away from your LV (love vibration).

WOKE BITCH CHALLENGE

Supporting your tribe with "How can I support you?"

This Woke Bitch Challenge is about dropping your "I was only trying to help" shawl and putting on your genuine "How can I support you" kickass cape. Know what I'm talking about? You offer unsolicited advice or opinions, and it ends up hurting the person who looked to you for support, then you justify your actions with "I was only trying to help."

Let's try something new. When a friend or family member comes to you with a problem, ask "How can I help? How can I support you?" Then, zip it and listen closely and lovingly to what they need. No advice. No solutions. No trash-talking. No shame. No blame. No guilt. This Woke Bitch Challenge is about shedding an outdated shawl that ain't serving and trying on a new cape that radiates love, compassion, and understanding. You don't have to solve the world's problems, sometimes you just need to listen, really listen. With this new cape, use the next two weeks to identify and utilize this game-changing question in situations when you need to listen like the superhero you are.

KEY TAKEAWAYS

- Speaking from a place of love and truth invites connection.

- Be honest about what you need. It is a courageous and liberating thing to do.

- Asking how to support someone who has come to you with a problem, instead of offering unsolicited advice and solutions, is an act of unconditional love.

CHAPTER TWENTY-FIVE

Manifest Your Dreams

Sometimes manifestation gets a bad reputation because people think it's a bunch of woo-woo bullshit, or some special skill to make something appear in your life.

Manifestation is a process of taking your idea, dream, goal, or vision and taking action steps to make it a reality.

Manifestation isn't about going after what your mind wants, but knowing who you are. Realizing who you are is realizing your essence. Who you are is the light and love that is beyond how you look, your personality, what you do for a living, and what you own. These are surface qualities that the mind grasps as important, but the true essence of who you are is deeper than this.

The prerequisite for true and powerful manifestation is to first realize the truth that you are beyond all surface qualities—your appearance, title, or possessions. For example, if you believe you are your appearance and wish to manifest a version of you that weighs less, manifestation will be difficult. However, if you put emphasis on the beautiful and formless essence of who you are, you'll find manifestation easier. It's important to watch the mind as it makes up narratives of how you need to be XYZ to be happy or manifest a situation different than the one you're in to feel whole. This is a slippery slope.

True manifestation doesn't arise from a place of need or

negativity—to be different, possess something or someone, or wallow in negative emotions. From a place of wholeness, there is power, wisdom, and gratitude. In fact, from this place of wholeness, there are good vibes all around. Then, when you lose the 15 lbs., receive the promotion at work, or get married to your partner, there is no difference in the good vibes you feel. You're already grateful for everything in your life (regardless of your life situation), anything that is manifested is icing on the cake. You won't depend on outside circumstances to make you whole or happy. When pleasant events manifest in your life, it's in addition to the good vibes that you already feel.

When you're in this state of joy and peace, and living in the present moment, you'll notice a shift in your life outcomes. Imagine you hoped to write a book. If your mind was constantly in unpleasant thoughts about the past or future, it would be very challenging to write. Imagine you sit down to write your book and your mind wanders to a writing class you took with the goal to write a book, but you never completed the class or your book. Now, you have a fear that the same thing will happen again. Also, you may have thoughts that no one will read the book once it is completed. In any case, your mind is active and caught up in the outcome. From a place of presence and joy, true creativity and inspiration takes place because your mind is empty of these thoughts of the past or future—basically any "what if" type of thoughts. Sure, thoughts arise, but with practice, you can keep realizing the truth of who you are that isn't these thoughts. You'll notice a new spaciousness within you that will allow for beautiful manifestations and creativity to come through.

E^2 EASY EXERCISE

You *are* what you seek

Fill-in-the-blank for this Easy Exercise:

Be the ___ you wanna see.

The blank space can be any quality or aspect of your life you wish to have present. For example: love, abundance, joy, prosperity, compassion, kindness, or confidence.

Here are some examples:

Be the inspiration you want to see.
Be the love you want to feel.
Be the leader you wish you had.
Be the wellness you wish to access.

Come up with your own *"be the"* phrases that align with you. When you manifest this desire, what will it look and feel like? What action steps do you need to take to reach your desire? How might you accomplish these steps or set of actions? Let these questions ignite your inner calling to be the magic that you want to experience.

WOKE BITCH CHALLENGE

Vision board supercharge

Create a vision board to help you embody your vision and live as if your desire is already here in your life. In this Woke Bitch Challenge, you'll create a vision board and place it somewhere visible for a month. Each day, you'll feel the contents of the vision board, so choose images and words that speak to you on a soul level. A supportive vision board won't be invisible or dull over time, it will grab at your heartstrings each time you pass it, sparking joy and adding a pep to your step each day as you actively live the life you wish to manifest.

Make your vision board online using Pinterest, Canva, or cut out words and images from magazines or newspapers or print your own pictures. Get crafty with it!

KEY TAKEAWAYS

- Be mindful of "needing" anything or anyone to be a certain way. Your wholeness is awesome.

- Imagine that what you want to manifest is already in your life.

- Divine inspiration comes through your state of being. To manifest your purpose, be in a state of presence (empty of thoughts and resistance), so the Universe can create through you.

When you pray for something, believe you have already received it and it will be yours.
-Jesus

CHAPTER TWENTY-SIX

#RelationshipGoals

So here we are in the chapter about relationships and guess what? It isn't about your current relationship status of single, in a relationship, married, divorced, or a combination of the above? These are labels, and it's difficult to dismiss these labels. When I gave an update of my relationship history to an acquaintance, I was immediately labeled as a serial-relationship person. This label had me questioning my choices and whether I was capable of a meaningful, healthy, and committed relationship with another person. I worried whether my past experiences were evidence that I wouldn't have the future I wanted. Does this sound like you? Were you sold on the idea that finding your better half, soulmate, or the right person, but it hasn't happened yet? Did you read another blog post about how to get the partner of your dreams?

What happens after you get the partner—how do you keep them in love and stay in love forever? Finding the partner we want isn't about strategies and plans for finding that partner.

Think about your ideal relationship and how you want to feel. Now, ask yourself how you can invite these qualities into your life right now, without the partner. When you cultivate a relationship with yourself, you become the partner you've always wanted. Those feelings of love that you get within a partnership are yours with or without someone else. This connection is the foundation for relations with anyone. Whenever I felt insecure in past relationships and looked to the other person to fulfill my needs, it was due to me not fulfilling some need I had.

For example, I attended several parties and networking events with past partners and wouldn't enjoy myself. Then, I wondered why my partner didn't notice that I was uncomfortable, tired, or ready to leave. This turned into a whole monologue. *C'mon, you know what I'm talking about.* Had I been attuned to my needs and honored a connection with my true self, I would have chosen to stay home from some of these events. Attending out of fear for the relationship won out over my need for comfort and rest. These fear-based motivators didn't quell any of the insecurity I experienced. So, what do you do?

Fill yourself with love from the inside out, so that you don't depend on someone else to feed the love that you want. Spend time alone to cultivate your connection to your true self. Be compassionate with yourself and accept yourself as you are—quirks, past choices, idiosyncrasies, and all the baggage. Why do we practice this? Because by cultivating these qualities within, we build the foundation for any external relationship. The saying, "You can't give what you don't have" pertains to this foundation of a conscious relationships.

A key magical ingredient in conscious relationships is acceptance. Yes, I know, it's not a sexy word, but I dare say this ingredient leads to a lot of magical tales. When we practice accepting the fun combination of traits that make up who we are, we can practice accepting the same in other people. The last thing we need in a relationship is to see the other person and remember only the shit they have done or said and their most unattractive qualities. This is not sexy.

When we practice acceptance in ourselves and others, it gives us compassion and empathy for even more human beings. When you hang out, it takes place in the present moment, and you can enjoy the presence of the other human being instead of living in your mental commentary around all their imperfections.

Try looking at your partner, family member, friend, or other loved one with fresh eyes, in the moment. Experiment letting go of the past (of what they did or said) and return to the present moment. This is a form of love.

The practice of letting go of the past, accepting the person in front of you as they are, and being in the present moment is so fresh and enjoyable. *Newsflash!* Relationships are meant to be enjoyed! To go even deeper, allow yourself to connect with the essence of who you are, the light within that goes beyond any personality traits or quirks, the love inherent in every being. Get cozy with your essence. Then get cozy with the essence of another person. To recognize these essences is true love, and the dramas of the external world don't stand a chance against true love.

E² EASY EXERCISE

You're Fucking Awesome Meditation

Choose an individual with whom you'd like to call forth more consciousness and connection. It can be a friend, family member, or partner. Part of bringing an element of consciousness to any relationship is seeing the essence of the person beyond their personality and external self. This fucking awesome meditation invites you to pause and reflect on all the good and wonderful qualities of the person you bring to mind. When an individual has been a challenge, this exercise is especially healing.

Take five to ten minutes in a quiet space and allow your heart and mind to fill with Universal Light. Now, picture the other person. Imagine the Universal Light filling them and surrounding both of you together. Focus on their inherent goodness to alleviate the narratives your mind creates and allow space in the connection. In this space, relationships blossom naturally with a focus on the present moment. For reals, connections can't blossom if we are making a list of all that is wrong with the person.

WOKE BITCH CHALLENGE

We Are All Fucking Awesome Meditation

This Woke Bitch Challenge is taking the Easy Exercise to the next level and expanding the recipients of your loving and fucking awesome well wishes. For eleven days, spend five to ten minutes each day to meditate on a selected (special) individual. Consult your heart and allow it to guide you to the recipient. If some tension with a loved one pops up, dedicate all or most days of this Woke Bitch Challenge to that person. Or choose to be like Oprah and give it away: *"You deserve well wishes! And you deserve well wishes! And you in the back—you get them, too!"* Again, with all *Easy Exercises* and *Woke Bitch Challenges*—no rules, just let your inner guide lead you!

KEY TAKEAWAYS

- If you're lost in the area of relationships, come back to yourself. How can you show up with more consciousness, love, and presence in relationship with who you are.

- Recognize the essence in another person that goes beyond form (appearance, role, or personality).

- To accept yourself as you are right now creates space to do that for other people. That is true love.

EMOTIONS ARE MEANT TO EMOTE.

PART 4
The Spirit

The Divine belongs to a formless and timeless dimension and is also within you. Connect with your essence by realizing the abundant and powerful support that is available to you.

CHAPTER TWENTY-SEVEN

Making Contact with the Divine (in You!)

I couldn't begin to explain Spirit without sharing my first experience coming into contact with the Divine. Although it is my belief now that the Universe is always with us—it wasn't until a palpable, physical, and emotional experience that I came to believe in a God and the Divine energy that surrounds us.

A few years ago in NYC, I walked by Grace Church in the East Village. I was lost in thought about something, but the church's open doors beckoned me to go in and have a look. The high ceilings, stained glass, and structure was vast, yet homey. This very old structure had the ability to shut out NYC traffic and noise better than newly built million-dollar condos. The quiet ambiance within the church invited me to sit with my eyes closed for what seemed like a few minutes. While my eyes closed, I felt a warm, powerful, and electrifying energy enter the crown of my head. This energy lit up every cell of my being. It felt as if I was floating with my feet off the ground. I was transported out of my body and out of the physical structure of the church. God's presence was strong and loving, dissolving any doubt about something bigger, beyond myself that I had consciously or subconsciously carried in my heart or mind. I was aware that I was having an unusual experience, but at the same time, I was at ease and comfortable, and surrendered to this loving grace. My soul felt God's grace without any thought. The busy mind that had plagued me upon entering the church was absent. The space within me was full of love and peace. Because I was in what felt like another realm or dimension—concepts like time or space didn't occur to me. When my eyes eventually opened, I looked down at my gray sweatshirt and saw that a good amount of tears had spilled from my eyes, creating wet spots. Crying wasn't something I am prone to, but somehow I wept without experiencing the physical sensations of the tears rolling down my face and cheek. What felt like ten minutes, a special timeless moment of awakening and resurrection, turned out to be forty-five minutes in human time. This left me in awe.

This experience opened me to the formless and timeless dimension and to the presence of the Divine. There's more space in my heart, depth in my being, and light in my soul having experienced the Divine, which confirmed what I read about and believed to be the Divine. My spiritual connection that day led me to a practice of opening my heart, surrendering to and trusting the Divine, and having faith in a greater power that carries me especially when I am having a hard time seeing it.

Please understand this is not a religious belief or understanding. If your religion or faith uses a different term other than God or the Divine, please use the term that resonates with you. The experience is the same.

E^2 EASY EXERCISE

It's a (spiritual) field trip, yay!

1. Check out a place that you consider spiritual or that you feel may welcome connection with the Divine. Temples, churches, mosques, shrines, nature lookouts, parks, and gardens are some examples.
2. Be open to Mother Earth's creations as the entire world is available and waiting to be explored with respect and love.
3. On your spiritual field trip, pack a nice beverage, snack, and journal.
4. Explore your chosen location with fresh eyes (even if you've been there before). Be open to any feelings or sensations that arise.
5. Jot down your experience in your journal. It's a great way to remember your connective experiences.

WOKE BITCH CHALLENGE

Make your own spiritual Lego land

This Woke Bitch Challenge is about taking the sensations you experienced for your Easy Exercise and bringing these treasured mementos home with you. Because next, you're going to DIY and construct this deliciously Divine place inside your mind's eye and keep it in your heart.

1. Journal on what this DP (Divine Place) looks like. When you're there, how does it make you feel? What messages of hope and encouragement are being offered to you?
2. Get as detailed as you want and go to town on it as if you were a kid with unlimited Legos and each Lego piece has magical powers and could represent, look, or be whatever you want it to be. The details, messages, and feelings of this DP are your Lego pieces.
3. Now, allow yourself to let go and build your DP. Your DP lives in your heart and is always available 24/7. It will never turn you down or tell you "sorry, we're sold out for tonight," like a desired hotel during peak season (great for the hotel, not great for the stranded guest). This is a total win-win situation. Staying at your dedicated DP won't cost you a dime!

KEY TAKEAWAYS

- Spiritual experiences vary from person to person—however themes of heart-opening, surrendering, and trusting in a greater power are often present.

- Encounters with the Divine often expand beyond man-made concepts, such as time and space.

CHAPTER TWENTY-EIGHT

God, Spirit, Source or Consciousness

(that which is beyond names)

You may have noticed that I use God, Spirit, Source, Divine, Universe, or Consciousness pretty freely and interchangeably.

I did this consciously, because I didn't want you to get hung up on a word. You may have a different understanding of something greater than yourself, as it should be. Let's go beyond words, concept, space, time, and form. Language is an awesome tool and gift (*hello, if it were not for language, this book wouldn't happen*), but language has limitations, too.

The point is—words are what we use as human beings to communicate in this realm—Spirit is beyond words and labels. Knowing how to use the word "spirit" in a sentence is different than knowing Spirit. *Know what I mean?*

I once heard Eckhart Tolle talk about words being pointers. He used an example of how as human beings we are quick to look at a flower and go, "Oh, that's a rose." But a rose is the name we attribute to this flower—the essence of the rose is so much more than the name or label we assign the thing. The essence of each rose is different, like human beings are different. Just because you have the same name as someone else doesn't mean that your essence or spirit is the same.

Instead, if we can get into the habit of saying, "Oh, that is what we call a rose," it would have a significantly different meaning because we would spend more time noticing and admiring the essence of the flower instead of simply labeling it. This type of reference invites you to go deeper into the essence of the rose.

The realm of Spirit invites us to go deeper and beyond our form to uncover who we are beyond our names, appearances, accomplishments, and relationships.

Put the label maker down

For human beings, it's natural to have a thirst for knowledge and to be in the know. For this EE, I invite you to take a day to notice your tendency to label something without knowing or observing the essence of that thing. For example, look at someone's shoes. Did you notice the brand of shoe and move on? What did you notice about the color, texture, and accents on the shoe? Did you see the way the shoe met the person's foot and the way they walked?

WOKE BITCH CHALLENGE

It's all in the details!

You're beginning to see how human beings label things and move on without seeing their essence. For this WBC, I invite you to slow down and watch your speech. This may be a bit odd at first, but experiment with removing "This is" from your speech. Instead, try "this is what we call a ____."

Sure, you may get some looks if someone sees your dog and goes "cute Shiba Inu!" and you respond with "this isn't a Shiba Inu. This is what we refer to as a Shiba Inu." You may find that removing the label allows you to take in the essence and special details of what is in front of you— the curled up tail and pointy ears of what we call a Shiba Inu. Perhaps you'll have a deeper connection with the dog, flower, or tree. Practice *Label Mindfulness* for at least a day and see how it goes! You may start a movement.

KEY TAKEAWAYS

- Words are tools we use as human beings, but Spirit is beyond names and labels.

- Knowing the name of something is different than truly knowing the essence of that thing.

- The essence of a person, place, or thing is beyond what our five senses and words can describe—it is a quality that goes beyond the surface.

CHAPTER TWENTY-NINE

Being Human and a Human Being

"You are a human being having a spiritual experience and a spiritual Being having a human experience."

When Eckart Tolle explained the words that make up who we are, my awareness of being human shifted. Have you ever reflected on what it means to be a human being or why these two words put together are significant?

The word "Human" means all the things we do in this world. It is physical and tangible—our bodies, minds, and how we function in the world. Being human includes our relationships with other human beings, our contribution to society, and embodies our response any time someone asks a question about us. It seems so ordinary and natural to believe that our function as a human being in this world and in this life is to go out there and do things.

Have you ever felt that what you "do" for a living isn't fulfilling or making a difference? This feeling points to the other part of you as a "Human Being."

What does the word *Being* mean? Your Being is the soul and spirit part of you. It is formless, timeless, and amazing. You don't have to take action or think it through. As the English language points out—we are human beings and

191

both the human and being element is within us.

How do you tap into the Being part within you and why should you pay more attention to Being? The Being part within you doesn't have a problem with any aspect of your life, especially what you have or haven't accomplished. The Being is like a light within that never dims. *Hello, how cool is that?*

In the Being dimension, there is complete wholeness, abundance, and no drama. Remember that feeling that something is off when you just do, do, do? Before being aware of my Being, I often had thoughts of, "I'm not meant to be a robot in this world and just do what you have to do. There's got to be more." This occurred when I did tasks such as a responding to e-mails, correcting papers, or inputting information into a system.

While you may not be able to eliminate these tasks and other things that you "have to do"—bringing "Being" into your "Doing" can greatly improve your joy and presence in each moment. The most effective way to activate your Being is to come back to your senses. As I'm typing this, I feel the texture of the keyboard on my fingertips and hear the tapping sound of my nails against the keys. I am aware of the roar of the Taipei buses outside the coffee shop and hear the soft music coming from the speakers. My nose picks up the aroma of the handmade coffee, and my eyes notice when I take a pause from writing, a linear line appears, blinking, waiting for my next word. Being aware of your surroundings while doing your task is balancing both energies. When was the last time you focused your senses to what you are currently doing? When you bring "Being" into your "Doing," you doing becomes less important because each moment is fresh and new with your awareness.

*Try it out: Bring **Being** into your **Doing**.*

- Regardless of what you're doing in this moment, tune into your senses.
- What is the loudest sound you hear? What is the softest?
- What does the air feel like on your skin?
- What details do your eyes pick up?
- What scents does your nose pick up?
- What do you taste?
- When the mind makes commentary or complaints on your experience or task in the present moment, be aware and move back to your senses.
- Keep returning to the experiences of the senses and refrain from labeling anything. For example, I'm drinking coffee from Congo, Africa. When I am sipping the coffee, my senses are on the experience of the coffee without labeling thoughts such as, "Oh, this is coffee from the Congo. It is supposed to have a fruity aroma. Hmm, how come I don't taste this? Is there something wrong with my palate?"
- After checking in with your senses and incorporating your Being—take a moment to pause. How did bringing your Being change your experience of what you were doing? Did you find it boring or mundane?

How does Being change the outcome of your doing and affect your purpose?

When you bring the aspect of Being into your Doing, it elevates the quality of what you produce. Have you ever tasted food that you know was made with love and care?

When a person loves and cares for the ingredients, loves the process of cooking, and cares for the people who will consume the food, the meal tastes better. This applies to anything and everything. If you work in a hotel, you check-in a guest while your attention is checked out (no pun intended), and sure, the guest still gets their room key and finds out when breakfast is served. However, when you are in your *Being*—the same actions yield a different experience for the guest and you. When you are in your *Being*, there is a genuine interest in making the arrival experience of this guest pleasant. The only thing required from you is your presence in the moment (the secret sauce is your Being) even though you have checked-in 100 guests and your shift is about to end. With your attention focused on *Being*, you'll be able to notice details such as the guest's empty water bottle or their toddler. You may offer to refill their water bottle or offer the child a coloring book. Had you been only in your *Doing*—your attention would be focused on getting the guests into their room as soon as possible with thoughts on the next task or what you'll do when your shift ends. Being elevates what you Do.

As Human Beings, it is our nature to bring our essence into this world while we continue to do and create.

This is how *Being* can change the quality of what you do, and it has zero dependence on what you do. Dishes, sweeping, sales calls, teaching, or winning the Nobel Prize.

Only the Mind wants to judge what it is you "do" and decide that some things you do require your presence while others aren't worth it. In our busy modern world, multi-tasking has taken us out of our Being and placed more emphasis on our *Doing*—productivity and results. The love and care that goes into our Doing is missing.

The added bonus of *Being* is your life feels purposeful. When there is attention focused on the present moment and what you are *Doing*, it's an invitation to the Universe to create through you. Perhaps you are currently in a role that you find isn't ideal because the purpose is missing. Try to bring *Being* into what you do and notice that opportunities that come your way are more aligned, the people you meet and experiences will burst with creativity. Mindless *Doing* serves no one, especially you. Blending your *Being* with your *Doing* allows you to take steps that will manifest your desires that you are currently too exhausted to see. *Inspiring, right?*

 ## EASY EXERCISE

Light up your task

1. Identify a task on your agenda that usually leaves you groaning. Is it laundry, dishes, paying bills, studying, or bathing your child?
2. Bring *Being* into the task you have identified. Some tips for doing this include eliminate multi-tasking, turn off electronic devices (especially notifications), and pay attention to your surroundings.
3. Record the experience of your task today. How did it feel? Was it challenging? Did it go by faster or feel different today?

WOKE BITCH CHALLENGE

Bring your (Being) to work-day

This WBC is best practiced at the beginning of your day for optimal joy!

1. Today, set the intention to bring *Being* with you throughout your day's work and interactions with other people.
2. Choose an item to carry with you that will serve as a reminder to *Be*. This can be as simple as a Post-it Note with "Being" written on it, a special bracelet selected for this purpose, or changing your phone background.
3. As you go about your day, let your item serve as a cue to pause and tune into your surroundings. For example, you may talk to a customer on the phone, and glance at your item to shift you out of your automated *Doing* and back into *Being*.
4. At the end of the day, reflect on three highlights in which *Being* was right there with ya!

KEY TAKEAWAYS

- The Human part of a human being can be thought of as things we DO in this world.

- The Being part of a human being points to the essence of who you are beyond form, names, and accomplishments.

- There is wholeness and abundance in the Being dimension—no mind-made problems or dramas.

- To bring the Being (Presence) into your Doing elevates the quality of your creations.

"I've learned that people will forget what you said, people will forget what you did, but people will never forget how you made them feel." –Maya Angelou

CHAPTER THIRTY

Own Your Humanness

Control and the need for control is pointing at a lack of trust in Spirit. When we feel fear, we want to control. Recently, I had a conversation with a friend where I expressed that I experienced a wave of all types of emotions and was reactive again. She gently said, *"You're human. Honor your humanness."*

The mind tries to make you believe that how you are at this moment is wrong, and you *should* be different. What does it mean to honor your humanness in a spiritual sense?

As a human being, you'll experience joy, fear, anger, jealousy, love, envy, sadness, and much more. You can still be a spiritual being on a higher vibration. Being reactive in a difficult situation is completely natural for a human being. When these moments arise, the solution and antidote is to offer yourself compassion. You know how warm and lovely it feels when someone tells you all is well and everything is okay. Nothing is wrong with you.

This simple act of compassion undoes the knot of self-created issues with our own humanness. The world doesn't need perfect people—the world needs more compassionate Beings that can accept their humanness and the humanness of others.

One of the most human feelings is fear, yet most humans have a big issue with this big emotion. In our culture, it is so undesirable for people to feel fear, we try to exert control over difficult situations. We want to control other peoples' behavior, schedules, the news, the weather, policies, and so much more. Even I, your Woke Bitch Guide, experience the desire to control another person's behavior. *Eeek!* In examining and watching my need to control and understanding that it isn't possible to control another person (at all!) and doesn't serve my growth—I was curious about where this need for control came from.

Control happens when our thoughts or feelings have a background of fear. If life was unfolding in a joyous, loving, and inspiring way, would you still want to control a situation or person? Of course not! You would allow life to flow through and around you.

Here's another question for you: When has your attempt to control a situation helped or worked? My guess is *never*.

It's okay that as human beings we want to exert control from time-to-time. The next time the urge comes over you, stay in your awareness that your desire to control comes from a fear. Get curious and ask, "What thoughts are popping up that make me want to exert control?" The exercise to explore and get curious about your desire to control shifts the energy away from a place of fear and controlling to a resting in awareness and gaining insight into your patterns. Throughout your exploration and discovery, continue to practice compassion and acceptance of your humanness. Your fears and need for control are invitations to be kind to yourself and honor who you are as a human being. Now, that's *Woke*.

We are at a very unique time in history. The collective sense of fear is strong and the need for control, stronger. Elizabeth Gilbert said in a webinar that the Coronavirus pandemic has the entire world feeling like their pacifiers were being yanked out. As human beings, we turn to control for comfort and security—our jobs, school, social interactions, status in society, ability to travel, our health—all yanked away. As a result, we are left with our curiosity, discovery, and leaning into our humanness.

E^2 EASY EXERCISE

Hello, Control Freak!

In this chapter, we talked about our tendency toward control being based in fear. For this EE, pause for a minute and reflect on a situation (small or grand) in which your inner control freak came out. There's no need to tell it to STFU or get out—instead, acknowledge your need for control as something you know and understand. Offer it a greeting, *"Hello, Control Freak"* with compassion for your humanness.

WOKE BITCH CHALLENGE

Level Up Faith and Surrender

This WBC is about taking the EE to the next level. Now, you have more insight into why your inner control freak shows up. We recognize that's part of our humanness. Thoughts perpetuating fear keep our inner control freak active, which affects our well-being. Let's give this inner control freak some TLC through faith and surrender. Turn to your faith in a higher power, choose to let go of your control, and let the higher power take care of the situation. It is a more soothing approach than letting your inner control freak fly—you feel me? Keep at this practice as long as it feels good.

Don't know how to surrender or tap into your faith? Try a simple line to the Divine, such as *"Hi there, I'm struggling a bit here. Please help me let this go."* There's more on prayer as a tool in the next chapter.

KEY TAKEAWAYS

- Honoring your humanness means accepting the full spectrum of feelings that arise without judgment.

- Choose compassion over perfection—this is what the world needs!

- Controlling behavior happens when our thoughts and feelings are aligned with fear instead of trusting that the higher power of your beliefs has got this.

CHAPTER THIRTY-ONE

The Formless Dimension Through the Power of Prayer

In the past, I never prayed. My relationship to prayer appeared in superficial ways such as on social media when an earthquake happened, and everyone would write, "Pray for XYZ Country." Then, you repost on your social media for likes.

My understanding about prayer has changed. Now, prayer brings me more life, vitality, joy, and a connection to something beyond myself.

There's no right or wrong way to pray. Your connection with God/Source/The Universe is your connection—your prayer doesn't need to "sound" a specific way. Start with something simple, "God, I am not sure how to begin but at this moment I feel XYZ and need your help"

In the moment you ask for help, there is communion with a Divine source. Human beings (you and me) have free will. This means we must ask for help before we receive Divine intervention. And we also have to keep in mind that we may not know what's best. We don't have the big picture view. Pray with ease, confidence, and humility. Surrender your questions to the Divine of your understanding's inbox.

Think of prayer as an email going to God's inbox with questions, concerns, and comments about your life, family, community, and the world. In some hotels and public spaces, you'll see a comment box, where they welcome you to give suggestions and comments. Unlike friends or family, or even your favorite restaurant, God is always open, 24/7. And They are ready to take your prayer any time and all the time. Pray as much as you want. Your prayer will never bounce. The Divine of your understanding has infinite power, so we can surrender our human issues. Don't hesitate, feel shy, or feel shame in asking for help. It's a safe space, I promise!

Be open to God's response. After sharing your prayer, you may notice guidance taking form in little signs that pop up throughout your day. For example, you happen to pass by strangers having a conversation and hear a piece of advice that resonates or a street sign jumps out at you. If these signs don't show up like this, don't fret—Divine Guidance comes in its own unique and amazing way customized for you. Be open to receive the answer to your prayer, even if it doesn't come in the package you were expecting.

E² EASY EXERCISE

Prayer 101

Here are a few techniques to jumpstart your prayer practice :

- Choose a quiet place—dim lighting may help you settle down. Pray anytime, anyplace.
- Take a few conscious breaths.
- Address your prayer to the Divine in your unique way. There is no need to address the Divine in a specific way.
- You may pray for peace for all Beings, guidance in a particular situation, a blessing for a specific person or a group of people, or say *Thank You*. Gratitude is a wonderful prayer.

Lately, my prayers have begun with gratitude for needs being met and for helping me release any thoughts, patterns, or habits that don't serve my highest and best Self. I ask God to help me let go of what isn't my true Self and help to evolve and grow in each moment so I can serve others.

There is no need to get specific in a prayer unless you want to. I find it most helpful and comforting when I surrender and allow God to oversee my journey and show me the way. This alone makes me feel lighter, less alone, and more at peace. Give it a try!

WOKE BITCH CHALLENGE

Metta 4 U, Metta 4 ME

I love the idea of Metta Prayer because it is like writing a devotional love song and adding lyrics that you gel with. Not only that, I find beauty in the format of how a Metta Prayer starts with offering yourself blessings first before spreading it outward. Seriously, we have to really be full of love to give love, ya know? So, get creative, get abundant, and offer yourself and the world a kick-ass blessing right now. Allow it to evolve as you do. Here's an example of a Metta Prayer to help you get started:

May I be happy, healthy, safe, and free.

May I recognize the light within.

May I be protected and guided by the Divine.

May I walk in love, grace, and truth.

May I be at peace.

May my family be happy, healthy, safe, and free.

May they recognize the light within.

May they be protected and guided by the Divine.

May they walk in love, grace, and truth.

May they be at peace.

This type of prayer is an expression of my devotional love song to myself and my family. To expand this, change the recipients to other members of your tribe, including:

- Parents, Siblings, Relatives
- Friends
- Your community
- The world and All Beings

Repeat the prayer and each time, change the audience receiving your Metta Prayer. Start with those closest to you and end with "All Beings." You'll feel all the vibes!

KEY TAKEAWAYS

- Prayer is a direct line to the Divine of your understanding.

- There is no right or wrong way to pray.

- Prayer and asking for help from the Divine allows the space for miracles to come through.

CHAPTER THIRTY-TWO

Tools to Connect with Spirit

We've all been there before—feeling uninspired, disconnected, and unable to tap into the deep well of amazing-ness that lies within the core of who we are. To be connected with Spirit is to have an inner knowing that all is well. Something more powerful that loves us is at work guiding us to our highest and best selves. Doesn't that sound wonderful? You don't need to have it all figured out. Surrender control and receive the gifts from the Universe that come in the form of abundant love, health, wisdom, and support.

The prerequisite to receiving these gifts is stillness. Mother Teresa once said, "God speaks in the silence of the heart." If you're thinking that you have too much going on, how could you possibly cultivate silence? If you're sweating it, here are some tools to utilize that will help you connect with Spirit. Please keep in mind that running out to buy a deck of oracle cards won't automatically connect you to spirit or bring about a deep well of peace. The most important ingredient is your willingness to be still and receive guidance from beyond. I am happy to report that this is absolutely free and available to all of us!

Easy tools

Prayer: Imagine prayer as one-on-one time with the most powerful, intelligent, loving, wise, kind, friendly, and compassionate Being, Evuh! This amazing Being also loves you unconditionally—nothing to change here! Also, this Being wants to hear everything you have to share, so there is absolutely no need to mince your words or fear being judged by what you have to say. Prayer is a conversation with Source, an outlet to share your dreams, fears, ambitions, and hurts. When you communicate earnestly during prayer, your soul plugs into the frequency of the Universe. On this level, your worries don't seem as gripping, and this stillness and wisdom from within is able to awaken. Before prayer, you're hostage to an endless to-do list and stresses of your life situation (work, relationship, family, health). During prayer, you hand it all over to Source. After prayer, you can be in the present moment and live your life minus all the things weighing you down because you know God has your back.

Oracle Cards: I admit I've gone from not using or owning any oracle decks to being an oracle-deck junkie. Oracle cards come in a variety of themes and images. Oracles cards are a great support for comfort, confidence, and assistance in making decisions. When you're flustered, agitated, angry, or stuck, these cards support you in moving forward. Often, the stuck feelings are because you've disconnected from Source energy and the Divine wisdom within you. If life throws the same issue at you on a different day, when you've had rest, meditated, and connected to Source through oracle cards, and you will have a clearer day. Oracle decks are affordable (unless you buy the whole store). These cards offer guidance and shine light on a situation no matter how you may be feeling. Think of oracle decks wanting to support you ESPECIALLY when things are rough because Spirit wants you to know they are always here for you. These cards are one way for them to convey their message of love.

There are many fun and insightful ways to work with the cards. Draw a card to start or end your day. This message can be something to hold in your heart as guidance and encouragement. Let the message sink in and bring you a sense of peace throughout your day.

Once, I encountered an uncomfortable situation in my work teaching at university. I felt unaligned and my students weren't catching anything and didn't want to be in class. This really made me angry especially since I hadn't encountered this before. I put in more effort and time than usual to customize and make the lesson plans as engaging, yet the anger and resentment bubbled inside me after class. I tried to sleep that night, but the emotions were like a fire inside. I couldn't rest or surrender. *The Angel Guide Oracle* deck by Kyle Gray called to me. I couldn't sleep anyway, so why not. I asked for guidance. The card I drew was a simple and beautifully illustrated, and its message brought me deep peace and allowed me to detach from my emotions. I realized that I had done my best, and it was not serving me to control or influence how they applied or didn't apply themselves in the course. The angel guide message wanted me to know it was not worth my time to be engaged in this life challenge. The best approach was to draw boundaries and just say "No." Don't worry, my heart knew that wasn't a "I quit my job" but a "No" that meant I wasn't going to place more effort and energy on the situation.

There are many types of decks out there. Choose a deck that you find attractive—it could be the artwork that features diversity in the cards, or you may like the wisdom in the words. Have fun, be open, and remember that there is no such thing as a *bad* oracle card—only love and support.

Spirit Writing/Journaling: This is a fun and enlightening exercise. What is Spirit writing? It's a writing sesh that takes place while you are connected with the Divine, your Higher Self, Spirit, or whatever you want to call the higher power. It requires simple tools, a journal and a pen or pencil (no typing here).

Sit in a peaceful place, calm your mind, and surrender to unlock your deep wisdom. Thanks to our ego, many of us have issues accessing our inner wisdom because our mind is cluttered with an endless to-do list or a running narrative of comments and complaints. Try a Spirit writing session any time you feel flustered, disconnected, or even in despair and *ready* to move past this with an open mind.

Come back to stillness. At the top of the page, write a question, issue, or a need for deeper understanding. A simple question that works well is "What do I need to know about my current situation relating to ____?" The next step is to invite your Higher Self, God, Source to come through your writing or perhaps invite a specific Divine Being—Angels, Archangels, Ascended Masters (Buddha, Jesus, Mary), Goddesses, or Spirit Guides. Invoke the Divine Being of your choice into your consciousness and ask your question or state your need for guidance out loud. Pause with your pen in hand and allow the writing to flow through you. Don't analyze or question what is being written through you—visualize yourself as an instrument of the Divine whose words are flowing through you. When you feel in your heart that you've received the complete message, take a deep breath in and out, and thank the guide for their wisdom. When you Spirit write, you may lose track of time. That's okay! There is no fixed period of time to complete a writing session. Sometimes, the writing goes on and on and other times, it comes through in a very succinct and concise manner.

Next is the fun and exciting part. Read what you've written out loud. I tend to avoid using the word "channeled" because it may give of you a woo-woo impression. Honestly, when I read what I've written in these sessions, they read like I channeled a Divine Being.

Be open to what appears on paper as it may not make complete sense to you at that moment. There is absolutely no obligation to save the writing for any specific reason—think of it as suggestions from the Universe. Do with it what you will. Be optimistic and know that this exercise may feel strange and uncomfortable at first, but you'll feel more ease with practice. This tool connects you to Source. Many of us have had a lot of dust collect around this direct-line, so it just needs to be cleared up.

Travel

This may seem like a strange way to cultivate a connection to Source, but travel can bring about a sense of presence—of being in the present moment. This isn't to say that going somewhere new will automatically make you more woke. When we are in a new environment, such as during travel, there is a sense of awe and wonderment that emerges. We aren't as involved in our mind's narrative as much because there are new experiences to be had, sights to be seen, foods to be tasted, and overall we are more attuned to our physical sensations. Through this inner body awareness, we are able to engage with the present moment, and the present moment is a portal for connecting with Spirit.

What can you do if travel isn't an option for you right now? I'm happy to report that this sense of wonder and awe can be evoked in your backyard, a local park, or natural setting. Of course, the lakes in New Zealand and beaches in Greece have left me breathless and filled with a deep sense of reverence for and Oneness with nature. These travel moments live within me, which I can recall anytime. However, with an openness to experience, I have felt the same awe, delight, and wonder when I wander down a new and quaint alley in New York or butterflies flutter on my roof in Taipei. I invite you to set the intention to free up space in your mind, drop the idea of getting to a destination, and allow yourself to linger, pause, and notice the beauty around you. Don't be surprised if you experience more connectedness and notice something Divinely inspirational with an open mind and intention to experience a Divine connection during your daily commute. The Universe is waiting for and wanting your exploration.

Workshops, Courses, and Retreats

Having been to many spiritual retreats, events, and workshops—it is energizing to share my presence with other human beings who are there for the same reasons—to connect deeper with our true selves, beyond our human experience and into a connection with Spirit. I regularly attended industry-themed events and conferences involving lots of talking, networking, and deal-making. In spiritual workshops and events, you're encouraged to simply "be" and not use your electronic devices. If you arrive early to the ballroom for the session, silence and meditation are encouraged. My biggest takeaway from these retreats wasn't hearing the well-known speakers, but the experience of being with a large group of present human beings who practiced living in the moment. These interactions were so different than most of my interactions with others where people are distracted or too busy being "stressed." You know what I'm talking about. When you can tell someone isn't quite "here" or listening. I've certainly done that before myself, too. The experience of sharing space with the other attendees was so uplifting and inspiring that I walked away feeling more connected with my deeper self and that stayed with me.

However, this connection with your higher self doesn't come automatically with attending a retreat and nor does it stay with you forever. It has to be nurtured and cultivated. As you consider the various tools available to you in the form of online courses, weekend workshops, pop-up events, and destination retreats, know that one isn't more effective than the other. The prerequisite is tapping into that stillness within you. Trust me, there is no retreat glamorous enough or teacher enlightened enough to transform someone who is unwilling or open to change. When travel isn't an option, there are a wealth of online courses by well-known and less-known guides. Online courses are mostly self-paced, can be significantly more affordable than in-person events, and remain available in your library. Online courses can be helpful, encouraging, and enlightening. Transformation starts from the inside-out, not the outside in. Therefore, be present and explore on!

E² EASY EXERCISE

Build your Woke toolbox

Research one of the tools listed in this chapter and have a casual chat with a practitioner or someone in your circle who has tried one of these tools. Let your curiosity guide you.

WOKE BITCH CHALLENGE

Connect with the Divine

Book or incorporate one of the tools for connecting with spirit. For example, if you chose to practice Spirit writing for this WBC, identify a time in which you are going to do the exercise without interruptions. Remember that intention and stillness are key ingredients for connecting with the Divine, so show up to your Spirit Writing as if you showed up to that long-awaited dinner reservation at your favorite restaurant—excited and ready to try! Whatever tool you choose to use, let it be purposeful and make yourself a clear and open channel for some magic!

KEY TAKEAWAYS

- The prerequisite for connecting with Spirit is stillness and receptivity.

- Prayer, Meditation, and Journaling are examples of easy tools to connect with the Divine.

- Use your tools with sincerity and openness to receive guidance and support from Spirit.

CHAPTER THIRTY-THREE

The Collective Consciousness

The Collective Consciousness is a big deal I know, but I don't let it overwhelm you. By being present, you heal the world. *Mic Drop!* Starting with self—are you showing up today adding love or fear? Awakening happens when you're present in a state of acceptance and unconditional love.

Collective Consciousness means we are all connected and have the power to influence one another positively or negatively. This doesn't mean that we can control others. Think of a time when something big happened in the world: war, elections, pandemics. Now do you remember how the day went for you? Did you experience waves of anxiety and nervousness that weren't associated with you or your day? This is the Collective Consciousness at work.

You may feel that there is so much chaos going on in the world right now, and it seems endless. A part of you wants to see this shift and change, but you may not know how. There's that fear and control button again. What if you could digest the wisdom that we are all connected and the action you take within you to change the world will be powerful in making change happen?

If there's chaos in your family dynamic, for example, and you feel a lot of angry energy—dare to be the calm in the situation. In whatever situation you are in—choose to be what you truly want more of. Don't scream in anger "Why are you guys so angry?" That adds more fear to your family and to the collective.

One time, I was annoyed with my parents who were chatting loudly in the car. I burst into their conversation with, "Why are you guys talking so loud?" You see what I mean? Be mindful of what energy or dynamic *you're* bringing to the situation.

Show up to your day being aware that you have a choice. Again, do you want to add love or fear? Yes, a range of emotions and reactions exist in our human world, but it comes down to love or fear. Everything you do, say, or think feeds one or the other. More than how big or dramatic this action is, realize that your ability to affect meaningful change starts from within you.

Imagine your Being as a gift that you carry. When you go to a rally—bring love. When you are with your family—bring love. When you are in a classroom—bring love. Everywhere you go, everything you do—bring love. Your loving presence will inspire others to tap into their loving presence, and soon you'll see that love ripple out into your community and the world. Imagine what would happen if we all showed up to life with presence and love? *Mind blown!*

E² EASY EXERCISE

Love or Fear?

Examine your everyday actions—are they born out of love or fear?

WOKE BITCH CHALLENGE

You are all you need

For twenty-four hours, create the presence you wish to feel. If you want more love, hold love in your heart. You are all you need. Your presence is all other needs, too. Are you skeptical about whether this will work or not? Get rid of all those thoughts. Put it into practice and observe for yourself. The greatest gift you can give another human being is your presence in love. Let your presence be the present you give the world today.

KEY TAKEAWAYS

- Awakening happens from the inside out—start with yourself.

- Changing the world begins with a subtle action or intention from within you.

- In whatever situation, choose to be what you want more of. Dare to be the calm in the chaos. Dare to be the Love in a time of Hate.

CHAPTER THIRTY-FOUR

What Doesn't Kill You Makes You Stronger

(Resilience during Challenging times)

No doubt, we are living in difficult times. Perhaps every generation thinks so. If you're finding it difficult to be still, meditate, or keep up with other practices for your well-being, *you're not alone, my friend.* For the last few years, it has appeared the world is falling apart at the seams and all the tools in the world are added pressure in your day-to-day. Your mind says, "You don't have time to be quiet or present right now—look at the news, the world is coming to an end!" Then, you have a desire to flail your arms and tell everyone your pessimistic and morbid thoughts.

Sounds chaotic, right? During this time, the spiritual community and many of my favorite teachers were recording and creating a lot of content to help people. Through listening to podcasts and watching the recordings, I found messages that resonated with comfort.

This isn't a time to step away from your tools. It is a time to strengthen and make them a priority. Your meditation practice and commitment to live life as it is in the present moment is more important than ever. When times weren't as challenging, these practices came with more ease. However, these practices and tools were created for difficult times. So don't shy away—rather, make mindfulness an even more integral part of your day, and let it be your anchor.

Use the tools and techniques you've learned to get closer

to the God of your understanding. You may be arching your eyebrows at me like *what does that mean*? Honestly when I first heard this said by Michael Singer—it moved my soul, but my mind couldn't intellectualize it.

So I asked, *"God, how can I get closer to you through my practices?"* The answer opened a new tender place within my soul. This one simple question and answer allowed me to shift any situation from one that appeared shitty with hate, anger, or resentment to one of love, empathy, and compassion. Sure, I experienced all the difficult feelings, but asking how I could be closer to the Divine also asked my spirit how I could become more like the Divine.

What can we learn from this? The information, wisdom, and knowledge you seek is found in compassion, gratitude and prayer. If I saw the violence on the news, I could get closer to God through having compassion for people in intense struggles, feel grateful for my safety, and pray for all beings in the world. This shifts us away from fear and into a serene and powerful place, which resides in each of us.

It's okay if you feel incredulous or resistant, but at some point, your soul and these words are gonna click. Feeling all the shittiness and world-ending rhetoric is exhausting and will never affect positive change. This is your invitation to lean on your tools, techniques, and inner knowing, and lean on the Divine to get you through tough times. Growth, peace, and *wokeness* await you!

 **EASY EXERCISE**

You are a badass

Reframe your predicament so you see challenges as the Universe showing you how much of a badass you are to overcome them with grace.

WOKE BITCH CHALLENGE

Form your Woke Squad

1. Make a list of people who support you.
2. Next to each name, jot down in what way they support you and/or how they make you feel.
3. Keep this list of your Woke Squad and never forget the amazing human beings who have your back.

KEY TAKEAWAYS

- Challenging times require your strength through the use of your spiritual tools.

- Your positivity can influence the world. The change starts from within you. Change your approach and perception first.

- Allow yourself to break open and get closer to God during tough times. Recognize the Divine in any situation.

CHAPTER THIRTY-FIVE

Believe in Miracles

(All is well in Divine Time under Divine Guidance)

Sometimes painful experiences can be the ultimate teacher and testament to the Universe's power to help you in the biggest way.

One summer, my rescue puppy, Nien, ran away. Nien was only six months old, hadn't been spayed yet, and had only been with us for a month and a half. My heart was gripped with fear. The night got darker, no one had seen which direction she went. It was a hot and humid June in Taipei, and my body started giving out. The mental stress of losing my puppy—mainly the feelings of fear and anxiety—drained my body. I was a walking shell wandering the streets of my neighborhood, feeling completely unequipped, devastated, and worried AF. That was a sleepless night. I lay awake with thoughts about Nien, where she might be, how hot it was outside, and worried about her safety. I wanted to find her so bad, but I was so grief-stricken, it was to hard function.

A search flyer needed to be created in Chinese, but as a non-Native speaker, I felt useless. My inner critic came out berating me for not having energy to create a flyer for my own dog and having to rely on others because of my language incapabilities. The next day, a search party was organized by the woman who helped me adopt Nien. She created and printed the flyers and got volunteers to meet and gather dividing the search into different areas. My anxiety, worry, and fear intensified the longer Nien was missing.

I prayed the night before to the Goddess of Compassion, Kuan Yin, and also my archangels for help.

As the day passed without sightings of Nien, my faith was tested. It was close to midnight, and the fatigue from the search was beginning to hit our bodies. The volunteers who were part of our search turned in for the night. My parents and I went back to a road where Nien had been seen the day before.

I told a couple passing by that I had lost my dog and pointed to my flyer. To my surprise, they had spotted her the day before, almost as soon as she had gone missing. They saw that she was wearing a harness with her leash and knew that she must've belonged to someone. They tried to go after her, but she darted out of sight. I couldn't believe that I ran into someone who had seen her. The couple suggested we check a parking lot nearby that had a lot of bushes and grass area. They thought that dogs were likely to hide around there for safety. They pointed to an area that was about a two-minute walk. We thanked them for the tip and walked toward the parking lot shouting her name and squeezing a squeaky toy. As we turned into the parking lot, we waited. Five seconds passed. Then, out of the bushes there she was.

We couldn't believe our eyes! I screamed her name and ran toward her. She didn't run toward us, nor did she bark. She appeared out of the dark in front of our eyes!

After thirty-two hours being lost, finding Nien safe and sound was a miracle of God's work.

The Divine timing of where, who, what, and how was

arranged by Source. We didn't know how we were going to find her, especially as my inner critic berated me for her disappearance.

The unfolding of this experience was the most powerful teacher reminding me that miracles can and do occur—especially when we need them most.

Miracle Finder

This is a shift in perception where instead of looking at the problems or faults, we look for the everyday miracles that keep unfolding in our lives.

Allow yourself to recall events from today or as far back as up to a week.

Ask yourself, what miracle or miracles have unfolded during this time?

A miracle doesn't have to be huge dramatic event, it can be a simple shift in perception such as having felt sad at the beginning of the day to feeling gratitude by the end of the day or a delayed appointment that allowed you more time to enjoy some quiet time. Be open to what arises!

WOKE BITCH CHALLENGE

The Spiritual SOS

When you are in a crisis or *shit has hit the fan* and that fan is on high, practice surrendering and trusting a higher power to help calm your nerves.

- Tell your inner critic to take a hike. Don't get down on yourself for feeling bad, unsupported, or affected by the situation at hand.
- Practice taking the situation moment-by-moment and know that God oversees your journey to peace and wellness even if you feel awful or are experiencing unkind thoughts.
- Repeat "I surrender to the Universe"(or use the word that resonates for your higher power) and feel yourself releasing your situation to the Universe for a complete resolution and knowing that the outcome may not be what you expect, but it will be what you need.

KEY TAKEAWAYS

- Miracles do exist. Expect them to happen for you all the time and use prayer as a tool to amp up your connection to these miracles.

- Even if you are emotional or caught in fear mode—know and trust that Source oversees your journey to peace, love, and safety.

- There is always Divine timing at work—surrender the details of how, when, where, and who.

CHAPTER THIRTY-SIX

Oneness

(Connection with everything and everyone)

You may have heard the saying that we are all connected, and it may go in one ear and out the other because it seems so cliché. But—we are all connected and influence one another.

During an orgonite-making class (Orgonite is a substance made of resin, metals, and quartz that balances and harmonizes bio-energy, otherwise known as orgone, chi, or prana), I was drawn to a flower design of overlapping circles known as The Flower of Life. I didn't know the meaning, so I asked the teacher. Being drawn to something you don't know is a good indication of a subconscious connection.

This geometric design has many ancient roots, but the teacher explained that these concentric circles symbolize our shared root or connectedness; and we are all collectively here to be one. There isn't a single person on this Earth who is "extra." Even the challenging people are meant to be here, and some teachers would say especially the challenging ones are meant to be here as vehicles for our collective growth.

Looking at the visual image of The Flower of Life can be mesmerizing. Oneness may not be your first instinct. When you look at the circles touching and overlapping, you'll see that it represents a grand imagery of our connection.

Our connectedness shows up as a form of synchronicity. For example, you just meditated on a certain theme, and this theme shows up in different areas of your day. Or, you think about somebody, and they reach out to you. A number sequence shows up repeatedly for you in different places. This realm of synchronicities is endless, and I'm excited for you to experience them as your awareness grows. Synchronicities are a wink from the Universe. You may find that it's more of a fist bump or high-five. Whenever they appear, recognize these synchronicities with gratitude to keep them flowing. Imagine Divine messengers having your back, but you're too busy scrolling on your phone—it would be difficult for Divine guidance to show up because your mind is occupied with other things. There's no space.

Think about experiences in your life that are beyond words and difficult to logically explain. Don't bother looking for the explanation. Think of it as fun, exciting, and a view toward connection.

During lunch at a retreat, I sat with hundreds of other attendees. I joined my family and waved hello to the other people sitting at the table.

A young man with twinkling eyes, a warm smile, who looked to be about my age, sat next to me. This young man was at the retreat with his mother, and talking with him was a breeze. We talked about the teachings and being present. While he shared a story about presence, he held out his hand with his palm up to illustrate part of the tale. In that moment, our eyes locked on each other.

All the sound, chatter, and background of the lunchtime meal faded away. It was as if we were looking into each other's souls. Although the intensity of the experience was uncomfortable at first, and I was more than a little self-conscious, it didn't take long for my thoughts to dissolve and to lean into the gaze. There was a deep connection of our essences. This Being in front of me was one-hundred percent here in the present moment and so was I. It was fascinating to share that type of experience with another human being.

Eventually, the gaze came to a natural end. My family witnessed the interaction in awe, because it lasted for more than ten minutes. If you've ever tried to gaze into someone's eyes for more than a minute, you'll understand. Try it. Seriously.

If you're eye-rolling or giggling to yourself, I can't help but smile, too. It's not something that happens everyday. In that ten minutes, we recognized our oneness and shared a depth of understanding.

Our souls are constantly connecting, even if our minds aren't aware of the interaction. This young man expressed that it was a "re-meeting" to him. He felt that our souls had met before and Divine time, space, and sequence of events brought us together in-person.

As lunch ended, the young man and I shared a hug. His loving energy will stay with me forever. This same loving light that is within him, that I got to see, is also within me, even if we never meet again in human form.

As you read this story, did your mind want to label the connection or relationship? Did you wonder if it was romantic or a love-at-first-sight type of experience? I get it. Our minds like to put experiences into boxes. However, the soul is timeless. It follows a path and is okay with not knowing.

My interaction with this man was a moment shared in true presence that was deep, warm, loving, and intimate AF, but it isn't what I would call romantic. It was a first-hand exploration of this oneness of all life.

 **EASY EXERCISE**

Soul Gazing

This EE can be practiced alone or with a partner of your choice for two one-minute intervals.

- Sit across from your partner or face a mirror if practicing solo, set a timer for one minute.
- Gaze into the other person's eyes or your own in the reflection. It may feel odd and silly at first but stick with it!
- Once the time is up, take time to record how it felt and if any insights came to you about the other person's essence or your own.
- Repeat this exercise again for another minute and observe what comes up in the second round. Was it easier? Did the essence become more accessible this time around?

WOKE BITCH CHALLENGE

Eye Spy Your Essence

For this WBC, take the practice of the EE and apply it to your interactions for today.

Your intention is to look at the essence of each Being (human or animal) you interact with today, and practice soul gazing.

You may be giggling visualizing how creepy you may appear—or you may deeply connect with another Being and spread more love today. For this WBC, refrain from telling people what you're doing and gaze at their Being. You may get your coffee from the same coffee shop as always, but today make intentional eye contact with the barista.

At the end of the day, reflect on how this WBC shifted your day. How did others respond to you? Don't be surprised if your gazing created a softening or a resistant response in others. The important thing is that you practiced going beyond the surface and spotted the essence of another.

KEY TAKEAWAYS

- Everyone serves a purpose in another's growth.

- Synchronicities are an example of oneness manifesting in our lives.

- Recognize the synchronicities in your life to welcome more.

- Sharing the present moment with another human being is a form of true connection.

CHAPTER THIRTY-EIGHT

Spiritual Adulting

(Recognizing your growth and realizing there are no mistakes)

Mistakes are an illusion because every experience moves you toward growth and expansion. You are better for the experience.

Spiritual Adulting is a commitment to you, your Higher Self. Do your best and surrender the rest. This way, you'll have no regrets.

Know who you are. You have all you need.

Take everything moment-by-moment because this moment is all you have.

"There are no mistakes" seemed like *BS* to me because a good chunk of my self-talk was spent in self-criticism and berating myself for my mistakes. When something turned out differently from what I had intended or planned, my conditioned habits were to look at myself and analyze what I had done "wrong." This is a hard one to reconcile in your mind, but with an awareness of your tendency to judge and criticize yourself, you'll learn to relax and be glad that you have this awareness.

Sometimes, when I step back, I'm blown away by everything I've learned and how much my life has expanded for the better. Have you ever done that? When we label something a "mistake," there are feelings of blame and shame, which keeps us small and doesn't allow for the growth and expansion we desire. Don't believe me?

Put your attention on your mistakes. How does that make you feel? For me, I'm not in the present moment and energetically stuck in the past. Thinking about your mistakes isn't empowering. You'll probably feel shitty, and your confidence takes a nose-dive, making it difficult to generate forward momentum. However, when you focus on the growth or even a single or subtle takeaway, you'll find empowerment and wisdom. All the challenges you go through, every heartache, fall, disillusionment, rejection, disconnection, imbalance, pain, and suffering has made you who you are today.

When it comes to spiritual adulting, I can't help but think of my parents. My wonderful, loving, and caring parents don't want a single painful or unpleasant thing to happen to me if they could help it. There are experiences that have happened to me that seem painful and that they would rather I wouldn't have gone through. Whether it is a health issue from exhaustion or a relationship they perceived as having gone on too long—they would rather it hadn't happened. If I was still drinking from the fountain of mistakes, I would feel horrible that my so-called mistakes worried my friends or family.

For example, I *shouldn't* have worked so hard in that sales job that compromised my immune system, and I *should* have seen earlier that there was no future with some of my relationships. We've all been there. Ruminating in the past allows our perceived mistakes to chip away at our power and sovereignty.

Radical, right? I am not saying I want to repeat any of these experiences or wish them on anyone for their growth, but I recognize that it's better that the experience happened because I grew from it. Experiencing pain helped me learn

238

about pain and discover tools for healing. Feeling loss taught me how to live with reverence and unconditional love for a loved one who has left this realm. Feeling heartache sucked, but I learned about self-acceptance and self-compassion. I am whole and unbreakable. I am grateful for all these lessons that taught me how to invite more joy, love, and presence into my life. This is the stuff that matters, and I am totally at ease with the unique and customized way that these learning experiences unfolded for me. How about you? How do you feel about your experiences?

I also don't want to diminish the pain and suffering caused by trauma. I'm sorry anyone goes through an experience that causes them pain. I invite you to seek professional advice and therapy for these deep wounds.

Over the past few years, there have been many opportunities, changes, and projects that required my focus and dedication. Writing this book was a long-held vision and was a significant challenge. Fearful thoughts lurked from background to foreground and questioned my ability and credentials to do this. That's a real creative buzzkill, I tell you. However, when I combine an intentional practice of doing my best and let go of the outcome, everything was supportive and aligned. Our best will vary day-to-day and moment-to-moment, but we all know when we've done our best. For me, this means being all in and one-hundred percent present, and emptying my tank for the day in a productive way but not in a sacrificial way.

Think of challenges as a relay race. You run your best race and then pass the baton over to God. You know your goal, but what if Source has an even better idea for you. Do you still want your first goal? Handing over the baton is about surrendering to a force that is greater than you and that is working for your highest good. You still have to show up and do your part, but you can let go of the outcome.

I have shared my experiences, stories, lessons, and tools with you in this book. My hope is that you can take all these tools and techniques into your knowing and create a life that is meaningful, happy, healthy, and present in this moment. That's is Spiritual Adulting!

 EASY EXERCISE

Introducing you

1. Now that you recognize your status as a WB, take a minute to reflect on your best qualities.
2. Imagine that you are about to introduce someone to a best friend—and this friend is the real you!
3. Write down what you would say about yourself and don't hold back on the good stuff!
4. Refer to this list as needed whenever you feel out of alignment.

WOKE BITCH CHALLENGE

Be your own advocate

Sometimes we diminish our inner guidance and defer to others for advice or next steps because of doubt. This WBC helps you power up on your inner guidance system.

1. Reflect on a current challenging situation in which you feel iffy, confused, or upset. Allow your mind to grasp the whole situation.
2. If applicable, reflect on how others have advised you on this situation and next steps.
3. Pause for a minute and allow all the voices of others to melt into the background.
4. Tap into your inner guidance system through slow deep breaths or a visualization of your choice. Allow your higher self to offer advice that is aligned with who you are.

KEY TAKEAWAYS

- Mistakes are an illusion—every experience contributes to your growth and expansion

- Labeling an experience as a mistake brings feelings of guilt and shame—not helpful!

- Refocus on the lesson from an experience no matter how small can help you feel empowered.

- Pain can be embraced as a fundamental catalyst for growth.

- A balance of doing your best and surrendering the outcome is a one way to feel good and aligned.

CHAPTER THIRTY-NINE

Rituals

(Choose your own adventure for your well-being)

Rituals are comforting and a sacred part of life and an awesome way to put into practice all your new tools. Whenever you feel lost and ungrounded, having rituals that touch and nurture the body, heart, mind, and spirit are powerful and grounding, especially when you travel or live in different places around the world. Rituals can provide a consistency in your life.

Rituals are different for everyone. On page 250, you'll find a table with suggestions to mix and match to create a ritual that works for you. A ritual that works for you will be one you do consistently. See how that works?

Choose at least one ritual from each column—body, mind, heart, and spirit. Know that each day and every moment is an opportunity to show up and be more authentically you.

Practice leaning into your rituals for support, nourishment, and expansion. These quick ritual suggestions are a great way to begin and end your day. They act as anchors for the life you want to live.

The nature of each day changes, so feel free to flow with the rituals that work at any given time. Notice if your mind gets fixated or turns the rituals into a strict regimen. Practice letting go and doing what feels right.

EASY EXERCISE

Choose your ritual

Review the tables on pages 250-253. Notice which ones you already incorporate in your life and which ones pique your interest. Get curious about your rituals!

WOKE BITCH CHALLENGE

Integrating rituals

For this WBC, use the Ritual Tables starting on page 250. Build an AM and PM ritual for the next seven days, which you'll practice incorporating. Set the intention to treat yourself to holistic rituals that fit the WB you are!

KEY TAKEAWAYS

- Rituals can be customized to meet you where you are on any given day.

- Rituals that address the mind, body, heart, and spirit contribute to your overall well-being.

- Notice when your mind wants to control the rituals and instead, allow yourself to relax and come back to the intention of self-care.

CHAPTER FORTY

Living in Alignment

Dear Beautiful Human Being,

Thank you for taking the steps toward self-care. In a world where we often feel pressured to go, go, go—the choice to look inward and practice self-healing is commendable AF. Looking inward can be raw, messy, and unpleasant at times. It can also be amazing, transformative, and change the trajectory of your life forever. As you say *wassup* to your inner self, you'll realize that this is an incredible gift to others and yourself. Everyone will experience the fullness and depth of who you are.

My hope is that you feel guided, empowered, and at ease with letting it all hang out. It's not easy to be a human-being. I kind of want to beat up the person who planted that thought in your head! *Oh wait, that would be Ego—dammit!*

It takes guts and courage to be kind and loving. I am so grateful you made this commitment to yourself. I've shared my stories and experiences in this book with you so we can laugh, cry, and recognize the Divine lessons in this experience we call life together.

God dealt each of us a very customized syllabus. The exact lessons each of us gets don't matter as much as the support and guidance from the Divine to move toward your authentic self. Maybe like me, you see some lessons in your syllabus that you'd rather play hookie or doubt your competence to take on. You've got this! As much as I would rather not have experienced some of my own Divine lessons, as I'm sure you have experiences you'd rather not have gone through, I can't deny they have contributed to the human being I am today.

The prerequisite for this course of life is being *you*. Yes, tools in all forms are helpful, but the most integral part for waking up to transformation is 100 percent you in your full and glorious presence.

Let what you've learned sink into every pore of your being and marinate in your soul. You have the strength, love, courage, and vulnerability to live your life purposefully— you *are* the strength, love, courage, and vulnerability you're seeking. And I can't wait for you to expand in your own unique and woke way.

Here's to pledging to be responsible for your well-being and honoring the Woke Bitch that you are with love and kindness.

Blessings and Love,
Marissa

CAN'T SPELL SPIRITUAL WITHOUT R-I-T-U-A-L.

CREATE YOUR EVENING RITUAL

I invite you to choose at least one item from each column to create your evening ritual. If you try and don't enjoy an item, choose something else until you have an evening ritual that works for you.

BODY	MIND
Choose your favorite pajamas	Meditate
Stroll out in nature	Listen to your favorite podcast
Play with children or animals	Yoga Nidra for Sleep
Eat a healthy snack, such as seasonal fruit	Watch a video or show that nourishes you
Take evening supplements or flower essence	Write what you did today and what you'll do tomorrow
Take an herbal bath	Turn off electronics one hour before sleep
Drink a cup of herbal tea for sleep	Read a fictional book
Do restorative yoga	Sketch, doodle, or color
Brush your teeth	Turn off social media

HEART	SPIRIT
Make a list of what your grateful for today	Sing a song to Spirit
Tidy up your home	Pray
Turn off the lights and light candles	Work with your oracle cards
Journal or Spirit Write	Light incense
Place crystals around you and on you	Use an aroma diffuser to clear your space
Look at your favorite photos	Listen to beautiful music
Send love and light to your family and friends	Work with your tuning fork or singing bowl
Sit in front of your altar in stillness	Take electronics out of the bedroom
Say words of love to yourself out loud	Lay in bed and quietly watch the world outside your window

CREATE YOUR MORNING RITUAL

I invite you to choose one item from each column to create your morning ritual. If you try something and don't enjoy it, choose something else until you have a morning ritual that works for you.

BODY	MIND
Stretch	Meditate
Yoga	Play a few songs that make you feel good
Take a brisk walk	Visit a farmer's market to take in the sights, sounds, and smells
Drink a warm glass of water upon waking	Make your bed
Have a matcha or coffee	Notice the space you wake up in
Do breathwork	Remove visual clutter
Drink a cold-pressed green juice or smoothie	Start your morning slow
Oil Pulling upon waking	Journal your intentions for the day
Eat breakfast	Listen to an uplifting podcast

What other rituals do you need in your life? Be sure to choose items that nourish your body, mind, heart, and spirit.

HEART	SPIRIT
Say an affirmation or mantra	Pray
Greet your neighbors and people you meet	Open the curtains and let the light in
Drink an herbal tea	Pull an oracle card for the day
Read something that uplifts you	Say "Thank you" before getting out of bed
Say a Metta Prayer	Walk around your home with your singing bowl or tuning fork
Make an offering on your altar	Visit your altar
Journal your feelings	Talk to Spirit/God/Goddess/Guides
Have a good cry	Use your intuition to choose today's outfit
Listen to an audio book	Shout at the top of your lungs, "Good Morning, World!"

RESOURCES

Below is a list of the tools, books, and teachers that have guided my *woke* journey. You will always be uncovering new stuff to level up your wokeness, so stay connected on my website for up-to-date recommendations. Let your curiosity lead you because you are divinely guided!

Meditation and Movement Apps

This is a list of apps that have helped me develop and sustain a movement and meditation practice.

Insight Timer – An abundant source of free meditations.

I Am – Schedule feel-good affirmations to pop up on your phone throughout your day to keep the vibes going.

Headspace – Meditation focused app to help you get in the habit of developing a meditation practice.

ClassPass – Explore different types of classes to find your jam!

Podcasts

Podcasts are such a fun and accessible way for commitment-free exploration. My favorite part of podcasts is to discover new people and get bite-sized nuggets of wisdom.

Spiritual Queen's Badass Podcast – Emma Mumford talks all things spiritual in a fun and sassy way.

Eckhart Tolle, Essential Teachings – Recurring themes of stillness, presence, and Being.

You Can Heal Your Life – This podcast is by Hay House with a wide array of spiritual authors and teachers.

Teachers (a.k.a. Woke Human Beings)
A sampling of incredible human beings whose teachings and teaching styles have resonated and inspired me.

Eckhart Tolle and Kim Eng – Go-to teachers to shift out of the ego and into the present moment and dissolving emotional pain trapped in the body.

Tara Brach – She talks on topics such as compassion, fear, and loss in a way that is soothing and insightful.

Pema Chodron – Buddhist wisdom about suffering, impermanence, and uncertainty in a gentle, deep, and wise manner.

Kyle Gray – Delivers life-changing angel wisdom while staying in his authenticity is a real inspo.

Michael Singer – Teachings that focus on surrender and letting go of your deep-rooted, negative beliefs, feelings, and preferences stored within that prevent us from living a joyous and purposeful life.

Sophie Bashford – Goddesses and Divine Feminine energy, and Sophie's book is juicy, informative, and powerful.

Gabrielle Bernstein – Gabby's books and oracle decks are dynamic and engaging and connect with real people on the path to awakening.

Jen Sincero – light-hearted spiritual advice that makes you laugh and works.

Marie Kondo – Tidying IS spiritual. Spark joy- as she would say to gain confidence in decision-making and a space that supports the bold and awesome person that you are.

Elizabeth Gilbert – For all the creatives out there. If your spirit is calling you to lead a bolder, more creative, and more expressive life, then look no further.

Don Miguel Ruiz – Simple teachings for a foundational, easy-to-understand, and timeless Toltec wisdom.

Flower Essences

Lotuswei – An array of elixirs and mists infused with flower essences.

Oracle Decks and Cards

Angel Guide Oracle by Kyle Gray

Isis Oracle by Alana Fairchild

The Moon Deck by Aarona Lea Pichinson

Flowerevolution Deck by Katie Hess

Online Courses and Workshops

Online courses and virtual workshops can be effective for your growth *and wallet-friendly*. You may enjoy the self-paced format. Like any course or class—you get out what you put in, so don't expect to watch the videos without putting what you learn into practice!

Sounds True – Many authors and programs to be discovered.

Hayhouse – Great authors and array of topics ranging from unicorns to financial abundance.

Retreats

The retreat experience is amazing each time for different reasons. Keep in mind that retreats can be pricey because in addition to course fees, there are transportation and accommodation costs, too.

Omega Institute, Rhinebeck, NY – Surrounded by nature, nourishing food, and feeling like you're inhaling wisdom by simply being in one place with options like relaxing and dining on campus or taking an immersive two-day workshop on a range of topics with visiting teachers from around the world.

Vipassana Meditation – Take place around the world and are free-of-charge or donation-based. It takes A LOT of dedication to complete this retreat.

Eckhart Tolle Retreats – The costs of the retreats can vary depending on location and duration, but there are some gorgeous international destinations.

Woke Bitch Tip: If there is a particular healer or teacher that resonates with you, sign up for their newsletter to stay up-to-date on events.

Subscribe to publishing house newsletters to get first dibs on upcoming courses, workshops, books, and retreats. Subscribers often get free mini teachings, too.

You can find me at www. marissahou.com
Instagram: @WokeBitchBook
LinkedIn: Marissa Hou

ACKNOWLEDGMENTS

Thank you, Universe, for my life experiences so this book could happen with all its richness. My journey has been custom-made, and I am grateful.

Thank you, Mom and Dad, for your support. I am so blessed to have the freedom to pursue what I love backed by your faith in me.

To my family, you guys rock and give this book texture, content, and juice.

To Aunt Cindy, you are the OG Woke Aunt, and I am so grateful you introduced me to ET.

To my cousin Emily, my fellow WB and sister—thanks for being an integral part of my growth.

To my cousin Amy, thank you for asking me a pivotal question when I needed it most.

To my friends, I thank you for your confidence in me to complete this vision.

To Daisy, my Reiki healer and dear friend who has shared so much divine wisdom with me, thank you!

To Mimi, I am grateful for the miracle that is our friendship.

Thank you to the Beta Readers for taking the time to read my book and offer me feedback.

Thank you to The Book Witch, Heather, for your guidance and support. You believed in my vision, offered me tools, and cheered me on to the finish line.

To the doggies in my life, your love and essence kept me going.

Lastly, thank you readers for supporting this book and being a catalyst for more Woke Bitches in the world.

ABOUT THE AUTHOR

Marissa is an author, hospitality professional, and speaker based in NYC. She has worked at the world's top hotel companies and institutions and continues to share her experience through teaching and speaking around the world. Marissa's love of writing stemmed from a young age, and *Woke Bitch* is her offering to readers on living their best life with courage and authenticity.

Marissa holds a bachelor's degree in writing from Sarah Lawrence College and a master's degree in Hospitality Industry Studies from New York University. She splits her time between NYC, Taipei, and where the Universe guides her.

You may find more information on Marissa and stay connected at www.marissahou.com, via Instagram @WokeBitchBook or on LinkedIn.